QVEEN OF THE SVN

A Modern Revelation

E. J. Michael

Mountain Rose Publishing
Prescott, Arizona

QUEEN OF THE SUN
A Modern Revelation
by E. J. Michael

Mountain Rose Publishing
Prescott, Arizona

To the Divine Sophia, Queen of the Guiding Ones, and to
the Whispering Muses.

Mountain Rose Publishing
P.O. Box 2738
Prescott, AZ 86302

ISBN 0-9642147-0-9

Printed in the United States of America at
Graphic Impressions, Prescott, Arizona.

Typesetting and layout by
Castle Rock Publishing
Prescott, Arizona

Cover design by E.J. Michael and Mia Michael.

Address all correspondence to E.J. Michael,
care of Mountain Rose Publishing.

10, 9, 8, 7, 6, 5, 4, 3, 2, 1,

Table of Contents

ACKNOWLEDGMENTS

I offer heartfelt gratitude to my wife, Mia, and daughter, Sera Maria, for their kindness, patience and support during the creation of this book, and to my loving parents.

Grateful appreciation also goes to Susan Stevens for her generosity, encouragement and practical advice — far beyond the call of duty; to Scott Mullen, Jud Parker and Adrienne King for their helpful comments; and to Frank DeMarco for his astute professional suggestions. Special thanks also to Alan and Paula Greene, Christopher McCree, and Teresa Woods — for our many enlightening discussions; to John and Trish Banta, Mark Frizzell and to Mark and Veronica Riegner.

And — at the risk of these words becoming a litany of names — I wish to thank Sally Pickert, Marge and Hirindra, Brad Isaacson, Trudy, Cary Graller, Shirley, Carma, Karen, Mary, Burdella, Dot, and the rest of the "talk-time gang," who inspired me in ways unknown to them.

Sincere thanks also to Linda and Scott Ball, Lollie, Angelina, Sandra, Melinda, Oana, Janet and all the folks at Lifeways who bore with me so patiently — and continue to do so.

And, lest I forget, thanks to fellow seeker, Ed Ebel, and to Charles, who climbed the mountain before us.

PREFACE

In October of 1971, I set out with my friends, Ed and Charles, on an excursion to Peru. Ed and I were barely more than twenty; Charles was nineteen. We were on a quest.

After several days in Bogota, Colombia, we spent three weeks in the sweltering Amazon River regions of Colombia and Peru. Then we flew to Lima, and from there to Cuzco, ancient capital of the Incas. For approximately six weeks after reaching Cuzco, we stayed in the high Andes north of Lake Titicaca, using the town of Juliaca as our base of operations. With the aid of Quechua Indian guides — descendants of the Incas — we sought to discover a legendary hidden valley, mountain retreat of an ancient Spiritual Order or Brotherhood.

Our experiences ranged from rigorous to exceedingly dangerous, and our journeys took us to some of the most breathtaking and picturesque landscapes in the world — from awesome, snow-clad ridges to steaming Andean valleys — beautiful beyond description. We believed we were venturing where no white men had gone before. The hardships were severe. Ed and I nearly died; Charles never returned. He was last seen disappearing into the fog of a narrow llama trail — against the advice of the Quechua guide — certain the valley we sought lay in the darkness below. My experiences in the Andes inscribed an indelible signature upon mind, heart and psyche.

When I returned to the States, I was gaunt, having lost close to fifty pounds — nearly a third of my body weight. But I would never lose my burning enthusiasm for the Quest — the spiritual adventure all of us are called to experience.

In the following years, my journeys took me to many countries of the world. Always I sought to pick up the threads of the ancient wisdom tradition — evidence of which exists in every country of the world — describing the path leading to the portal of Initiation. Passage through this portal is denied no one who becomes inwardly worthy; those who enter experience a spiritual birth into what the ancient world called the

Mysteries.

I lived in Europe more than six years and spent three months in Mexico, much of that time exploring the ruins of the great Mayan civilization. In a variety of settings and on several continents I was privileged to study modern expressions of the Initiate wisdom — what some have called the Perennial Philosophy — twentieth-century revelations of the ancient secret teachings.

My destiny eventually took me to California and the American West, where I married and started a family. Throughout my journey I have gathered the seeds for the adventure you now hold in your hands.

Many of the events described in this story are true. Others are fictionalized versions of actual happenings. Still others are metaphorical in nature. It is the author's hope that this narrative will inspire the reader on his or her own personal voyage of discovery. If readers are prompted to clarify their own life perceptions — and to quicken their footsteps on the pathway to the Mysteries — this book will have served its purpose.

E. J. Michael
July 1994
Prescott, Arizona

QVEEN OF THE SVN

A Modern Revelation

*"Let those love now
who never loved
before.
Let those who always
loved, now love
the more."* — *Anonymous*

Pervigilium Veneris

BOOK ONE
Into The Inferno

"All earth comprises
Is symbol alone;
What there ne'er suffices
As fact here is known;
All past the humanly
Wrought here in love;
The Eternal-Womanly
Draws us above." — Goethe

Chapter One
THE DISCOVERY

"Life is either a daring adventure or nothing."
---Helen Keller

A ll my life I had been a seeker. In my youth I had developed a passion for the "hidden side" of things, and through the years remained forever charmed by the notion that it was possible to live a life imbued with love and joy. During my college days I had adopted the classical ideals of Truth, Beauty, and Goodness as models of inner striving. And though it was true that I had often lost sight of these philosophical icons — straying into realms of personal and professional futility — never before had I stumbled so far from my path.

Melissa and I had drifted apart in recent months and our marriage of six years tottered perilously near an abyss. Both of us were artists at heart, frustrated in our attempts to balance creativity with economic demands. Her vexation with me was not surprising. At thirty-five, driving a courier truck part-time for eight hundred dollars per month, I was a classic, career underachiever. We had house payments to make, and a three-year-old child. Melissa's scanty wage from the flower shop was not enough to make ends meet. And she longed to spend more time with little Angelina, just being a mother.

But a deadbeat I was not. For some time I had been writing articles and submitting them to magazines, and I had a modest portfolio of cartoons — in the style of the *New Yorker* or *Saturday Evening Post*. I longed for a breakthrough in my artistic work. In the meantime, financial pressures were threatening to fracture our marriage.

Feeling more like a failure each day, and hoping to turn things around, I had finally agreed to go with Melissa for relationship counseling. On a blistering afternoon in September, we had gone with Angelina for a picnic on the northern California hills overlooking the Pacific. It promised to be a new beginning.

Instead, we argued over petty disagreements, and the gloomy coastal fog and an unexpected drizzle splashed cold water on our plans. We discovered the worst development upon our return home. Somewhere along the ocean cliffs I had lost the precious gold and lapis medallion which Melissa had given me before our marriage. In addition to its considerable material value, it had always symbolized the love that held our relationship together. Might not losing the medallion foreshadow more serious losses?

Events in the evening seemed to support that ominous conclusion as Melissa and I fell into angry words and accusations. The simmering resentments reached a boiling point and the pressure made us explode. The scene was ugly and we wounded each other with our fury. In an instant of violent rage, I dashed our costly wedding china against the kitchen wall. I could hardly believe it was me cursing at the top of my lungs, hurling Angelina's tiny chair onto the patio, smashing it beyond repair. At least no blows had been struck; that was not our style.

Banished from my home in the aftermath, I took refuge for the night in a shabby motel. The sultry late-summer day which had started so promisingly was coming to a chilling end, and my whole life had begun to unravel.

I slammed the door behind me and threw myself despondently upon the musty bed. The cramped, smelly room was stifling and depressing — an ironic match for the emotional prison into which I had wandered.

My daughter's image seized my mind and I dammed up the tears. God, how I loved her! The thought of hurting her was unbearable. Now it seemed unavoidable.

In my misery, I remembered the opening passage from Dante's immortal classic, *The Divine Comedy,* which I'd once read while stranded in a small, southern Italian town, waiting two days for a train. The great poet described becoming lost in a dark wood in the middle of his life's journey. Dante found his soul's guide; I was still floundering in the shadows.

I stared blankly at the mottled ceiling, my mind churning. Things had to turn around. I could not suppress the conviction, springing from deep within me, that a far superior life was yet within our grasp. I firmly believed that a Higher Power was always near at hand if we would unite with it in our minds and our hearts. After all, that had been my major life focus since my late teen years. Had I traipsed in vain across five continents in quest of life insights? Must I now admit that I was a spiritual failure as well? My behavior that evening could hardly qualify as enlightened, even by the most liberal, psycho-babble standards.

I tossed restlessly on the sagging mattress, vividly awake. A dull pressure, expansive but not painful, built up in my head. It pounded relentlessly, silently, upon the limits of my conscious mind, as if it were a forbidden presence seeking entrance from the plutonian underworld of my unconscious. Something was assailing me, attempting to break in.

I sensed the peculiar inner guidance which I'd so often felt at dark moments in my life, coming as a subtle, strong feeling. My mind could challenge the conviction, but I was moved to trust the power of this unmistakable inner knowing. Something big was imminent — something decisive. I rolled out of bed and headed for the door.

Walking into the chill night air, I hurried along the quiet streets of San Rafael. At two a.m. there were few cars on the roads. I wandered aimlessly for several minutes, trusting the strange instinct that gave strength to my steps. I'd always been compulsive, but I felt this impulse was coming from a deep source. I walked beyond the shopping district, approaching the San Rafael Mission, one of the original Spanish chapels built along the "Mission Trail" by the indefatigable padres of New Spain.

I strolled into the chapel courtyard beneath a slice of silver moon. Gazing up at the statue of the Archangel Raphael, which stood guard above the massive church doors, I felt a lifetime away from the turbulence of that evening. This was one of my favorite spots in Marin, a county singularly blessed by many kinds of beauty, both natural and man-made. I melted into the shadows near the old sanctuary. Barely visible against the wall was the weathered, wooden statue of the Madonna, which I had often admired.

Though not Catholic, I had grown to appreciate the feminine side of Divinity, sadly lacking in so much of modern western culture. To unravel the mystery of the divine feminine in the world had become one of my current passions, and I had recently consumed a number of books on the subject. Regardless of what one might think of orthodoxy, and I certainly found it stifling, the Blessed Mother seemed to embody the highest ideal of Woman's Spirit.

Under the silvery crescent, and the inscrutable gaze of the wooden Madonna, I soulfully asked the higher powers to guide and direct me so that my life would be useful and my feet would be set upon the path of my destiny, a path I dimly sensed, but had virtually lost.

My mood was magically transformed. The spark of goodness and spiritual light in me burned more brightly. I resolved to mend the recent wound with Melissa and begin afresh. We would survive. More than that, we would thrive.

I hurried past the historic mission chapel and jogged back to the motel. Feeling inspired, I scribbled a short poem to Melissa — something I hadn't done in years — wishing I could come up with better words to express my love. Despite the lateness of the hour, I felt surprisingly alert. I slipped from my room again, ducked into my car and started driving to the coast.

Half an hour later, I parked beside the hill near the Pelican Inn, the scene of that afternoon's ill-fated picnic. Throwing open the trunk, I pulled out the metal detector I had borrowed that day from a close friend, in hopes of finding the lost love token. Initially, I had thought to try my luck with it later in the week, but the crazy impulse wouldn't let me wait.

I pushed aside the brambles and thorns and trudged up

the dark, lonely hillside. The ocean breeze chilled me through my thin jacket. Within minutes I had found the site of our picnic, not far from a twisted, stunted oak. I flicked the switch of the metal detector and set the sensitivity controls, then began to comb the grass, listening and watching intently. Before long the small speaker chattered with the characteristic crackle of discovery. Bending down to my knees, I soon wrapped my fingers around my cherished, golden pendant. I laughed aloud and shouted at the sky, hardly believing it had been so easy.

I stuffed the lapis treasure into my jacket pocket and turned to go. Noticing that the metal detector was humming even more loudly, I stopped in my tracks. With the aid of my pocket knife and flashlight, I began to pry and scrape in the coarse grass and flinty earth. After about five minutes of frantic digging, I was again rewarded in my search.

I pulled out a rectangular metal box, caked with soil, not more than twelve inches in length. It was apparently made of iron or steel; by the glare of the flashlight I could tell it was badly rusted. I shook it and something rattled inside. Though perhaps insignificant, the box filled me with curiosity. Turning hastily, I started back down the hill to my car, and was soon on the road to San Rafael.

Back in my motel room, I easily broke the hinges of the rusty box. Inside was a circular metal container, not much bigger than a cigarette pack. I carefully scratched the dirt from the metallic object and rinsed it for several minutes in the sink. The metal was darkly tarnished, but not rusted, and appeared to be silver. A peculiar design on the top looked like some type of hieroglyph. On the bottom left-hand corner of the underside of the case were stamped the initials, S.F.D. The curved top of the container was joined to the bottom half by two hinges at the back and a clasp at the front. I gingerly pushed at the clasp and gently pried open the box.

The smell of decay made my head turn. A damp, decrepit cloth hid an object beneath it. The material, obviously decades — if not centuries — old, crumbled in my hands. Trembling

The design on the face of the medallion

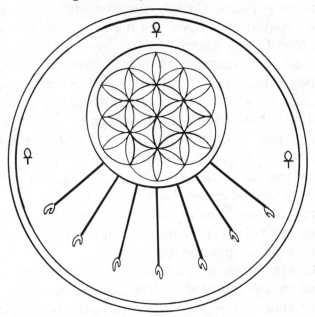

The design on the reverse side of the medallion

with anticipation, I delicately removed the object, which shone with a dull, golden lustre in the dim light.

It was a round jewelry piece, or medallion, apparently of gold, twice the size of a silver dollar and nearly the thickness of my little finger. The underside was dominated by an ornate disc, apparently representing the sun, with seven rays streaming out uniformly from the bottom portion of the sphere. At the end of each ray was a delicate hand, like that of a loving parent about to caress her child. Within the solar disc were seven interlocking circles which formed at each of their centers a symmetrical flower of six petals. Around the edge of the medallion, encircling the sun, mysterious glyphs stood out in relief. Egyptian hieroglyphs, I thought.

I turned the marvelous artifact over and stared in breathless amazement. On the medallion's face, in bold relief, knelt a beautiful, winged goddess of the ancient world, formed of splendid blue stone — most surely lapis lazuli — with streaks of silver and faceted jewels set into the gold. The eyes of the goddess were midnight black, and behind the crown of her head blazed a disc of ruby red — the disc of the sun.

The craftsmanship was by far the most exquisite I had ever seen on a coin or piece of jewelry. I felt certain it was a representation of the Egyptian winged Isis, most beloved feminine deity of the ancient world.

A golden chain of intricate design passed through a ring at the top. The medallion and chain together probably weighed less than five ounces. Yet I felt certain I held a treasure in my hands, a priceless artifact of antiquity, or at the very least a clever copy, in itself worth a small fortune.

Gradually my excitement was eclipsed by perplexity. What was the medallion's origin? How did it arrive on the hillside overlooking the Pacific? And why was I the fortunate one to discover it?

Instantly it occurred to me that perhaps I was not so fortunate. I had read of the so-called "curse of the pharaohs" that had followed down the ages those who had tampered with the cryptic treasures of the ancient, royal tombs. Was the medallion really that old? If so, who had brought it to California, then lost it?

The mysterious letters — S.F.D. — stamped on the box seemed so prosaic compared to the medallion itself. I presumed they were a clue to a link in the medallion's chain of ownership.

A bizarre sensation filled my soul and I was gripped by a feverish desire to solve this mystery. At the same time, a surge of greed — an emotion I thought I'd long since transcended — swelled inside me. I determined I would not part easily with this jewelled goddess.

Had I been able to foresee the events soon to befall me, I would certainly have thought otherwise.

Chapter Two

ULYSSES BUNDY

"To solve a puzzle, first spill all the pieces." E.J.M.

I awoke before five a.m., having slept barely two hours. Still clutching the golden Isis, I rolled from the bed, fully clothed, and left the motel. I had soon to leave for my delivery job, but another priority occupied my thoughts.

I made the four-mile drive to my home in less than ten minutes. Quietly entering the house, I found Melissa and Angelina still sleeping. I stared lovingly at them in their beds, grateful for having been blessed with such a beautiful wife and daughter.

Before leaving, I hastily appended a note to the verse I had written to Melissa the previous night, extending an olive branch and seeking pardon for the previous night's explosion. It read:

Think that the sun is illusion,
Think that a diamond is dew.
Think that to hope is delusion,
But know that my love is for you.
Dearest love,
    Please forgive. I love you dearly and am
so sorry for my angry words and actions.
Let's begin again. I have a wonderful
surprise for you and am certain our
fortunes are about to take an amazing turn.
          all my love, Jason

I could not have imagined how prophetic were my words.

Moments later, I softly left the house and was soon speeding south on Highway 101, through Marin county, toward the Golden Gate Bridge and San Francisco. For nearly half a year I'd been working for a small delivery company, similar to Federal Express but tiny by comparison, called L.T.A. The pay was minimal, but I enjoyed driving around the Bay Area, delivering small parcels and materials, mostly between law firms and corporations in the financial district, and for major banks, financial companies and their clients. I had become familiar with "silicon valley" and enjoyed the scenic beauty of the Palo Alto area.

My first stop each day was the Federal Reserve Bank on Market Street in San Francisco. I picked up material which I presumed was somewhat sensitive and delivered it to a branch of one of the nation's largest banks, south of the city. Some of my experiences had been most unusual.

On one occasion, several months earlier, I had to make a pickup at the Fed late in the day. Because no one was allowed in the inner sanctum of the nation's central bank without clearance, I had waited patiently for nearly half an hour for the package to be brought downstairs. An inner prompting urged me to speed things up and I brazenly told the guard I could wait no longer. Boldly stepping by him, I bounced up the stairs.

No one stopped me and I entered some private offices, announcing myself. While waiting innocently in the forbidden chambers, I saw articles, charts, and material on desks and walls which I realized were not for the uninitiated. A large, heavyset woman, obviously a manager, saw me and nearly hit the roof.

"Who let him in?" she shouted, trembling with barely concealed rage. "How the hell did he get upstairs?"

Several employees scattered to get out of her way, and moments later a nervous young woman handed me the package. We exchanged signatures on the delivery form, and off I scampered down the steps.

I had often reflected on the incident, the odd behavior of the manager and staff, and of the peculiar materials upon which my eager eyes had fallen. The events of that day and what I had seen would soon cast light on the bizarre web of circumstances in which I was about to become entangled.

My deliveries on that September morning were routine, and enabled me to think about the enigmatic medallion. I was so excited about the discovery that I wasn't tired, despite lack of sleep. My second hot espresso of the day helped, too.

In the late morning, I got a call on the radio to pick up a parcel at the Federal Reserve Bank in the city and deliver it to Dr. Ulysses Bundy in Woodside, north of Palo Alto. Twenty minutes later, the large sealed envelope was in my hand and I was speeding south on Route 280. Since my departure from home in the morning, I had dropped off my dusty Toyota Tercel and was driving in one of the bright, blue and white company pickup trucks.

I had delivered to Dr. Bundy about a dozen times and always found it fascinating. President of Chemical Bank — one of the world's largest — Bundy was an exceedingly wealthy, influential man. His home in Woodside, an affluent silicon community, was like a modern country palace. I had often seen four new Lincoln Continentals parked in his spacious, circular driveway. He employed a team of gardeners and maintenance men, always on the job at his impressive home, the grounds of which were immaculately landscaped.

I turned off the highway and minutes later pulled into the driveway of Bundy's palatial estate. I rang the doorbell and waited expectantly, hoping he would answer the door, as he had done on several occasions. More than once I had asked him questions about business and economics, and he had indulged me with precious minutes from his busy schedule. He was an impressive man, highly educated and brilliant. His remarks had indicated a fine grasp of the details of history and a remarkable insight into the forces that influence world events.

I smiled, remembering him once answering the door at seven a.m. in his pyjamas. He had warned me about the dangers of precious metals when I had brashly asked him what he thought of gold as an investment. It was an absurd question, as it was all I could do to keep from bouncing small checks.

The door opened and Ulysses Bundy answered. "Good morning, Dr. Bundy," I said, smiling. "How's everything?"

"Very well, thanks." Bundy was wearing a blue business suit — obviously not his day off. He was probably sixty, and tall, with an athletic build. A natural executive, he exuded power. Even his cologne smelled authoritative. His blue eyes and square features betrayed no emotion, yet something about his mouth gave me the impression of someone enjoying a mysterious private joke.

"How are your precious metals doing?" he asked with a trace of a smile. "I haven't seen the price of gold go anywhere recently." His attempts at sociableness struck me as being insincere, a mannerism. Social pretense masking an emotional coldness. He refused the pen I offered for his signature and pulled his own from his shirt pocket.

"I'm steering clear of the markets these days," I said, playing along with our game. "I'm sitting on the sidelines waiting for a really big move."

"Very wise of you. Better let cash be king than play roulette with the investment markets."

A strange feeling came over me — perhaps a prompting from an obscure, inner dimension. Possibly it was the resentment of a poor man suddenly wishing to become the peer of the wealthy elite. For whatever unseen motive, I made an impulsive decision which forever changed my destiny.

Shoving my hand in my pocket, I pulled out the mysterious medallion and dangled it before the banker's gaze. A feeling of pride overpowered the caution that should have held such a wild impulse in check.

"I've had the good fortune to come across this lovely jewelry piece recently," I boasted. "What do you think it's worth?" I handed the medallion to Bundy and he examined it carefully. Beads of perspiration formed on his brow and he momentarily paled, before quickly regaining his professional composure. Assuming his strong and inscrutable features, he returned the golden pendant to me. I realized, despite his nonchalant manner, that I had blundered.

"A beautiful piece. It appears quite antique. May I ask where you found it?"

My skin flashed hot. It was all I could do not to turn and bolt for my truck. "It's sort of a long story. I guess you could say I picked it up along the way. I'd love to talk more about it but I know how busy you must be, Dr. Bundy. Anyway, I've got a few more deliveries still to go and I..."

"How much do you want for it?" the banker asked. His question startled me.

"I...well...I hadn't really thought about selling it. I'm not sure..."

"I'll give you five thousand dollars," said Bundy, trying to be matter-of-fact. "I have a collection of ancient art and often contribute to museums. I'm sure your piece isn't worth that much, but I want you to feel good about the transaction."

"I was stunned by Bundy's offer. Five thousand dollars! My mind reeled with images of what I could do with the money.

"Ten thousand," Bundy insisted. "I'll make out the check right now." He drew a checkbook from inside his jacket and took his pen from his shirt pocket.

"I...that's a very generous offer, Dr. Bundy. Thanks, but I need to think it over."

The banker frowned slightly and the muscles of his jaw tensed up. "Think it over, then," he said. "Call me tonight or tomorrow if you like." He gave me a business card. It struck me as odd that a man as wealthy and powerful as Bundy would even have a business card, and it was comical to think that he'd hand it to a down-in-the-heels courier.

Bundy hesitated a moment, as if carefully selecting his words. "Don't let an opportunity like this pass you by," he warned. "The difference between the wealthy and the impoverished is often the latter's tendency to procrastinate. I assure you my offer far exceeds the relic's value." Bundy tried to be cordial, but his words were tight, almost angry.

"Thanks so much, Dr. Bundy. I'll definitely give it a lot of thought and be in touch real soon." I backed awkwardly from the banker's open door. "Thanks again, and I guess I'll see you next time."

I smiled weakly and headed toward the truck. I could feel his gaze follow me as I slammed the door, turned on the engine, and pulled out of the driveway. Sweating heavily, I looked in the rearview mirror and was surprised to see how tired and bloodshot were my eyes. The elation I had felt for the past ten hours dissolved into a sea of doubt and confusion.

Chapter Three
ON THE RUN
"Not only are the best things in life free;
they are priceless." E.J.M

I raced through my last deliveries and sped toward the company office in the city. Parking the truck in the small lot, I hastily walked into the office, depositing the keys.

As I got into my small Toyota, I noticed a man in a pickup truck parked a few spaces to my left, his engine idling. Something about him was vaguely familiar.

"Damn," I muttered under my breath. I had forgotten to pick up my paycheck. Abruptly stopping my car, I threw it in reverse. As I lurched back into my space, the pickup to my left roared forward, missing my car by inches. Had I not stopped and reversed at that instant, I would have been hit broadside, and possibly killed.

Killed! I realized, stunned, that the driver had *intended* to kill me! He slammed on the brakes of his pickup and got out, cursing, a heavy claw-hammer in his hand. His truck, still idling, blocked my escape. I sprang from my car, terrified. There was no time to consider why I was a murder target, barely time to react. My retreat was checked by the six-foot brick wall of the parking lot. The thug with the hammer came toward me.

I had no weapon and was easily a hundred pounds and several inches smaller than my adversary. I glanced about for a bottle, a stick, anything! Some rocks in the parking lot caught my eye. I picked one up, the size of my fist, and ran behind my car. Ten feet away the man paused an instant, sizing up which way to attack.

I had always loved baseball, and had, in more youthful years, taken considerable pride in the accuracy of my throwing arm. Raising the rock behind my head, I feinted a throw, judging my assailant's response. He only smiled menacingly and took a step forward.

I hurled the rock with all my strength and hit him squarely

in the throat. He grabbed his adam's apple and staggered away. I jumped into his idling truck and drove it to the side. Sprinting to my own car, I threw myself behind the wheel and drove past him as he clutched his throat and gasped for air.

I turned the corner into the street, raced forward and slammed on the brakes in front of the L.T.A. office. Running inside, I grabbed my paycheck and tore out again.

"What an idiotic thing to do," I told myself, speeding north through the city. Fifteen minutes later I was on the Golden Gate Bridge, driving through the fog.

Fatigue had vanished. My body was pumping with adrenalin, fear, and confusion. Who was that man? Why did he want to kill me? I racked my brain, trying to place the strangely familiar face. Everything fell together in an instant of awful realization.

I had seen the would-be killer that very morning at the home of Ulysses Bundy. He was one of his employees! I had presumed he was one of the gardeners, but he obviously wore other hats.

Bundy had sent him to kill me, and to steal the medallion. It would have been easy to discover the location of the L.T.A. office. And they wouldn't stop now. They would track me to my home, anywhere. I laughed aloud, crazily triumphant that I had been lunatic enough to stop and get my last paycheck. I would probably never see the L.T.A. office again.

Surely, the medallion possessed fabulous importance! Its monetary value alone could not have motivated Bundy. Money, for him, was not an issue. I was struck by his use of the word "relic" in describing the piece. Impossible though it seemed, he apparently recognized the medallion. What had moved Bundy to attempt this crime? What power did the ancient pendant hold?

An accident on the freeway forced me to take a roundabout route. I drove up Sir Francis Drake Highway, skirted the freeway, and pulled into the driveway of my home. Melissa would still be hurt, not wanting to talk at first. My mind reeled to think of the danger in which I had so foolishly placed her.

I walked through the kitchen and found her watering the plants on our patio. Angelina was riding her tricycle.

"Hi daddy, look at me. I've been helping mommy." I picked up my daughter and hugged her tightly. Melissa glanced at me briefly, then turned away. Her lips were tight, her jaw set, the way they only were when she was angry. Her pretty features had turned to stone.

"I'm sorry, love. I didn't mean to hurt you." I still held Angelina, not wanting to let her go. "We need to talk right away."

Melissa's brown hair shone in the late-afternoon sun. She hesitated, muscles tense, not wanting to speak.

"I suppose," she finally said, "you expect me to thank you for the note and say, 'Oh love, I'm so happy to see you.'" She mimicked her sweetest voice. "Forget it, Jason. Grow up. You barge in here as if nothing has happened and expect everything to be perfect. You'd better start seeing a counselor. I can't keep going on like this." She looked at me fiercely, then went back to the plants. The warmth in her deep brown eyes had vanished, though the fire remained. The pain I saw in them made me wince. I felt desperate; we had so little time.

"I've got something for you, Melissa," I said, pressing the lapis pendant into her hand. The look on her face softened.

"You found it!" she said.

"That's not all I found. Melissa, please listen. Something very serious...someone tried to kill me today."

She looked at me doubtfully, but saw I was sincere. "What! Why would anyone do that?"

"Well, you would've done it yourself last night," I said, managing a smile. I turned off the water and took the hose out of her hand. "Melissa, it's true and I'm very scared. We've got to do something quickly."

The ice melted from her eyes. She looked at me with the deep, soulful gaze that had so often broken down barriers between us in the past. "Who tried to kill you?" she asked, taking my hand.

"The whole thing is mind-boggling...unbelievable. It's because of this." I pulled the silver box from my pocket and removed the dazzling medallion.

Melissa gasped. "Where'd you get that? What is it?"

"I'm not really sure what it is, but it's very old and obviously very important. I found it last night on the hill by the ocean. It couldn't have been more than three feet from our pendant." I gestured to the love token in her hand. "I made the mistake of showing it to someone. I guess he knows what it is. Melissa, I know it's hard to believe, but Ulysses Bundy, president of Chemical Bank, tried to kill me. This thing is huge, and we're in deep trouble."

"Are you sure it was him?"

"Not him personally. He sent someone. But I'm positive." I couldn't bring myself to tell her how much money Bundy had offered me for the piece. "Look," I continued, "there's only one thing to do."

"Call the police and give them the stupid thing," she said, pointing at the medallion.

"No! I can't do that. Not yet, anyway. Besides, who would believe my story? We'd still be in danger. Those guys have so much power."

"What guys?"

"The financial elite. The Big Bankers. You know."

"You're just being paranoid, Jason."

"Listen," I said, "we're going to have to do something radical. I already know too much, having survived that attack. I've got to go into hiding. And we'll have to protect you. I think we'll have to call the police after all."

"We really should," Melissa nodded.

"But not the way you think. Don't mention the medallion. We'll have to make it look as if you think I've gone nuts. You think that maybe I'm going to hurt you, or steal Angelina, or something."

"Oh God, it just sounds so crazy. I can't take another one

of your adventures, Jason."

"We've got to, love." I paused an instant. "It'll be just like college," I said, repeating one of our oldest private jokes in a clumsy attempt to lighten the tension. "We've just got to pray and believe that things will work out. But if I don't hide right away I won't live through the night. And I can't let this medallion fall into the wrong hands. It must have tremendous importance. I think it's a kind of talisman, or something."

We were interrupted by a loud knock at the door. I looked at Melissa, trying to control my panic. Her eyes grew wide with fright. The knock came again. Louder.

"Go to the door," I whispered. "If it's them, I'll run out the back. Remember, you know nothing about the medallion." I put my daughter down and grabbed a knife from a kitchen drawer. The thought of maybe having to use the knife frightened me as much as anything else.

Melissa walked to the front door and gave me a long look, revealing both her love and her terror. I held back, not knowing whether to stay or to disappear out the back door. Melissa looked through the peephole for what seemed to be forever.

"It's George!" she said. "George Fort!" She laughed, breaking the spell of tension, then opened wide the front door.

"George, am I ever glad to see you!" I said, springing through the kitchen to greet our friend.

George took a step back, his eyes wide. "Believe me, I didn't do it! I didn't do it!" he said, holding his hands above his head in mock surrender. I was still clutching the big knife, my eyes bloodshot, my features strained. "Were you expecting the Internal Revenue Service, or something?" George asked, lowering his hands. Melissa took him by the arm and led him into the house.

"Sorry to startle you, George," I said, placing the knife back in the drawer.

"I guess you really got him mad this time, huh, Melissa?" George said. He was tall, with jet black hair and piercing dark eyes.

Melissa smiled weakly. "I wish it were only that," she said. George was a neighbor — a talented artist — and one of our best friends. We had often helped each other out, and I had confided in him when I needed someone who could listen and offer sound judgment. It was George who had lent me the metal detector the previous day.

"George, I don't know how to tell you this," I began awkwardly, "but we desperately need your help."

"No kidding!" he said, leaning back against the kitchen counter. "Let me see...your California dream's become a nightmare, and you're moving to Arizona to hunt rattlesnakes for a living."

"Listen, George. Someone tried to kill me less than two hours ago. It's a long story, but they won't rest until they've finished the job. I'm going to have to go into hiding. Now!"

"Who would want to kill you?" George asked, realizing my desperation.

"They want something I've got. I can't go into the details now. I need your help to get me out of here. And I need you to help Melissa."

"I'm with you all the way, Jason. Just tell me what to do."

With Angelina playing nearby, the three of us huddled together in the kitchen and swiftly worked out a plan. George would be instrumental both in my escape and in Melissa's strategy to protect herself and Angelina. The two of them would spend that night, perhaps longer, with George's wife, Jenny, and their family.

Melissa and I rushed frantically around the house, gathering a few of my belongings. I snatched Angelina into my arms and squeezed her, tenderly caressing her hair.

"You're my treasure girl," I said over and over again. Melissa and I embraced. She was sobbing softly.

"It isn't fair. It's just not fair," she whispered.

"Oh Melissa, I'm so sorry. I love you so much...you mean everything to me. Please pray for me. Don't worry...I'll be in touch soon. I love you." I softly touched her cheeks, now wet with tears, and kissed her for the last time. She forced a smile, and I waved as I ran with George down the driveway toward our cars.

"Daddy, daddy, where are you going? I wanna come!" Angelina cried.

"I'll be back real soon, love. I'm just going for a ride with George. I love you, treasure."

Slamming the car door, I took a last, grim look back at everything that was dear to me in my life, then gunned the engine and drove off.

Chapter Four
TAKING REFUGE

"Truth is stranger than fiction, and to most people is far less acceptable." E.J.M.

George followed me in his car and we were soon on the freeway, going north. We drove through Petaluma and headed to the Sonoma coast, driving continuously for almost two hours. As the sun began to set, we pulled off the road beside one of the awe-inspiring Pacific cliffs of the California coastline. I left a hastily scribbled note on the dash, grabbed my belongings, and jumped into George's old Mercedes.

The note said:

The BITCH doesn't love me. All's not well.
There is no God. THIS LIFE IS PURE HELL.

We wanted my assailants to think suicide. At the same time, Melissa could play up the fear of my faking it, then coming back to harm her. That way she would have police protection, or so we hoped.

We drove through western Sonoma County, through Sebastopol and Santa Rosa, then north on the freeway toward

Mendocino County. I had friends there, Ricardo and Deborah
Schuller. Their home was deep in the woods and off the beaten
track.

For most of the drive George and I were silent. He knew,
or could imagine, what I was going through, and respected my
need to be quiet. The shock and strain to my body and nerves
caught up with me, and I closed my eyes for over an hour. As
I drifted in the twilight world between sleep and waking, I
tried in vain to formulate a plan for my immediate future. I
was relieved, at least, to be going to Ricardo's.

He and Deborah lived in an idyllic setting among the
redwoods. They had built their home themselves, and had a
large organic garden. I had met Ricardo fifteen years earlier
when we were students at Emerson College in Sussex, England.
Ricardo was a native of Argentina, but had spent most of his
life in Europe and America. He and Deborah had met at Find-
horn — the famous, experimental spiritual community in Scot-
land.

Ricardo was a deep thinker, and we had enjoyed many
stimulating conversations over the years. While in England, we
had shared a most remarkable experience.

We had been on a long hike beside the cliffs of Cornwall,
near legendary Tintagel, an area permeated with Arthurian
lore and legends of the quest for the Holy Grail. We had spoken
that day on various spiritual matters of mutual interest. Ricardo
believed in the existence of powerful historical objects, such
as the Holy Grail, and the shroud of Turin, in which, according
to legend, the crucified body of Christ was wrapped before
burial in the tomb.

He said that such objects, often called "relics," became
invested with the particular spiritual qualities of the historical
moment in which they were involved. They were imbued with
almost supernatural, metaphysical attributes by their association in the lives and destinies of transcendent personalities —
individuals whose lives and deeds changed the course of history.
Such beings we often referred to as Initiates, Adepts or Masters.

We became so absorbed in conversation that we failed to pay attention to the approaching darkness. Wandering off the trail, we found ourselves in a thick mist. It began to rain, and we realized we were quite lost and ill-prepared to face the elements. As the darkness engulfed us, we were soon unable to see. Yet we could hear the roar of the Atlantic surf pounding against the cliffs below. The rain turned to sleet, and our feelings of foolishness turned to acute anxiety.

Becoming increasingly confused and desperate, we noticed a light coming toward us in the blackness. We moved toward it and shouted so as not to miss the opportunity. Moments later, a figure became visible, holding a small flashlight and dressed in yellow raingear — a gaudy phantom in the night.

He spoke not a word, but motioned for us to follow him. We walked in silence. Within minutes he led us to a road in that isolated stretch of western Britain. Pointing in the direction of the nearest town, he handed us the flashlight. We thanked him profusely for his help and asked if he really could afford parting with the "torch," as they called it in England. His reply astonished us, and lit a fire in our minds which would never die.

"Gentlemen, you have more need of the light than I, for I am not lost. This external light will guide you now, but you must kindle the light of your souls still more brightly in order to illumine your path from within. In time you shall know that the Grail of which you speak is within your grasp even now. I speak of the interior Grail...your spiritualized heart. Lose not sight of the true goal."

With these words he disappeared into the ethereal darkness of that Cornwall night. Ricardo and I, in recalling our experience later, both felt we had been privileged to meet a man whose remarkable powers were those of an Adept — that exalted spiritual Type about which we had so often conversed.

As George drove his Mercedes through the gathering darkness, my thoughts drifted back to that day in Cornwall. I wondered if I had found, in the strange Egyptian medallion, an ancient relic or talisman of the sort which Ricardo and I had spoken.

I yawned and stretched as we neared the town of Calpella. "Thanks for helping me out, George," I said.

He looked at me sympathetically. "I haven't done anything yet. So far, it's just been a pleasant drive in the country." There was a moment of silence. "I'm really sorry all this had to happen," George continued. "Do you feel like talking about it? I mean, I still don't really understand what's going on. What do you have that someone would want to kill you for it? You're nearly as poor as I am."

"I found something, George, that may be worth a fortune; perhaps it's priceless."

"You tell me all that and then won't tell me what it is! I'm gonna burst at the seams!"

"I'll show it to you soon. It may be an artifact of the ancient world. Why I should discover it is beyond me. Apparently it has enough value to persuade one of the financial elites to kill for it."

"Financial elites?" George said, raising his dark eyebrows. "What do you mean? Who do you think tried to kill you, Jason?"

"It's not a matter of speculation. I'm certain it was Ulysses Bundy, president of Chemical Bank."

"Jeeminy!" George exclaimed. "We're talking the Establishment here. I thought maybe it was a gangster type...the Mafia or something. Are you sure it was him?"

"Positive! I told you about how I got to know Bundy through my courier job, didn't I?" George nodded. "Of course, he didn't do it personally. He used a hit man, just like Hollywood." I then explained my encounter with Bundy at his estate, and the ensuing attack in the parking lot.

We were quiet a moment. George was sitting bolt upright, churning inside, his fists squeezing the wheel. I could feel his mental energy.

"What's the matter, George? You seem more excited than

me about the whole thing. I suppose you're going to tell me that all this fits into your paranoid conspiracy theories." Ever since I'd met George, almost five years earlier, he had often harped on one of his favorite themes, about which I was fascinated yet skeptical.

George was convinced of the existence of a semi-secretive, international power clique operating behind the scenes of financial, corporate, media, and government institutions. The goal of this shady, mysterious group — according to George — was control of the economic and political life, and ultimately of society itself. At first I thought George was just gullible, allowing himself to be taken in by wild notions of the "lunatic fringe." Over the years, I had gradually come to accept that some of what he said was true, though I was unwilling to admit it publicly. Not only was the subject controversial; it was just plain sinister. Above all, I didn't want to be seen by my other friends as being "paranoid" — just another artistic crank.

"I don't know what it is you've found, Jason, but Bundy's not an ordinary banker, for God's sake."

"What do you mean? He's head of Chemical Bank, and incredibly wealthy. Are you trying to tell me he's part of your international power elite trying to rule the world?"

"Dammit, Jason! Don't you get it? He's a member of the Trilateral Commission."

"The Trilateral Commission! How'd you find that out?"

"I saw his name on a list of all the members...just a few nights ago. You've really got yourself into some deep yogurt."

I strained to comprehend what this new revelation might mean. The Trilateral Commission, I had reluctantly learned, was one of the most exclusive, prestigious and powerful organizations on earth. It was also one of the least understood by the general public. Though not entirely secretive, its existence was known to relatively few Americans — nor did they realize the immense influence of the Commission and its members in shaping government and corporate policy, both domestic and international.

It had been formed by David Rockefeller, one of the wealthiest and most politically active financiers on the planet. Its members were among the most powerful movers and shakers in the fields of business, finance, banking, industry, education, the media, and government. Many of those groomed for positions of high office came from the ranks of the Trilateral Commission. The name "trilateral" derived from the three geographic and geo-political areas out of which most members came: the United States, western Europe, and Japan.

A domestic counterpart to the Trilateral Commission was the Council of Foreign Relations — the CFR — organized in 1921. Highly secretive, unknown to the majority, the CFR was nearly a ruling establishment in the U.S. Its elite membership dominated high cabinet and government officess, and also saturated top media positions, not only analyzing and interpreting policy, but determining it.

I didn't believe the Trilateralists were malicious in any ordinary, common "criminal" sense of the word. Most of them were undoubtedly decent people with families, hopes, dreams, challenges, and difficulties, like everyone else. What made them different from the ordinary person was their membership in a secretive clique of exceedingly wealthy and powerful individuals. If what George believed were actually true, some of them were apparently inspired by a monumental ambition: to rule the world.

George was convinced that their plans to create a New World Order and a One World Government would lead to a steady erosion of individual liberties. It would be a type of Orwellian, totalitarian state, in which the individual became a dispensable "economic unit" to be manipulated, "managed," and controlled, according to the dictates of the ruling elites and their "social planners."

Although I tried to reject the "conspiracy theorists," I had read enough reliable literature to know that the Trilateral Commission and the C.F.R. not only existed, but wielded enormous influence. What I found especially disturbing was that,

for some strange reason, these immensely powerful organizations were practically ignored by the establishment media.
Regardless of the accuracy of George's world view, it was clear
that our government had become a monstrous bureaucracy,
increasingly tyrannical in its power, something to be feared.

We headed off the main highway onto a two-lane road.
My mind whirled, trying to fit everything together. My sense
that the ancient medallion must possess hidden attributes was
becoming a strong conviction. Could it be that an elitist like
Bundy knew of its power and coveted it for arcane reasons
having to do with achieving political or economic domination?

"Looks like we're almost here," George announced. "You'll
have to navigate from this point." He pulled the car into a
service station and we telephoned Ricardo and Deborah to
make sure they knew we were coming. Melissa had called them
from San Rafael after we had left.

George spoke briefly on the phone and nodded to me.
"Let's go," he said, climbing into his old Mercedes. I directed
him along a dirt road that twisted for eight miles back into the
woods. Twenty minutes later, we pulled up the gravel drive to
a cozy house nestled among the stately, coastal pines. I stepped
wearily from the car, a fugitive among the California redwoods.

Chapter Five
UNSEEN POWER

*"Our fears are like fences. We must jump over them
to discover new territory."* E.J.M.

The next morning, Saturday, was a perfectly beautiful day, so typical of California at its best. I awoke to the smell of strong coffee, the aroma of which always had the power to get me going.

Having arrived at midnight, exhausted, I had gone right to sleep. Ricardo and Deborah were content until morning to hold their curiosity in check.

At breakfast, I sat at an antique, wooden dinner table, admiring their rustic cabin. One of Ricardo and Deborah's passions was using only organic, non-hybrid seeds in their gardening, and I noticed that one whole room was used for drying and preparing seeds. My friends waited patiently for me to tell them what crisis had precipitated our unexpected visit.

"You'd think that at my age I'd have learned enough to stay out of trouble," I said. "It looks like I'm in way over my head this time."

"What kind of trouble, Jason?" Deborah asked, pouring me coffee. Her dark, pensive eyes revealed her concern. George had told them only vague generalities, leaving me to describe the details.

"I may as well jump right in. I just hope all of you aren't dragged into this mess with me."

Ricardo studied me carefully through his spectacles. His silver hair was combed straight back, and he wore a trim mustache and Van Gogh beard — conjuring the image of a bohemian philosopher.

"Don't think of it in those terms," he suggested, "We are your friends and we'll do whatever we can to help. After all, Jason," he said with a twinkle, "you know very well that I have friends in high places." Ricardo pointed his finger in the air.

"We'll need them, Ricardo. Yesterday someone tried to kill me. And not just anyone. It was Ulysses Bundy, President of Chemical Bank."

"That's incredible!" exclaimed Deborah. "Are you sure?"

"Absolutely," I said, then told them of my meeting with Bundy and the parking lot thug.

"I don't understand why he would go to such an extreme," said Deborah.

"I would have taken the five grand," George commented.

Ricardo shook his head. "What would motivate such a wealthy man to attempt murder?" he asked.

"It doesn't seem like the behavior of a cultivated member of the ruling class," Deborah said.

"To say the least," I added. "I admit it just doesn't make reasonable sense. He can't be driven just by greed for money."

George was silent. But he had the imperious look of someone who knew the answer to a puzzle and waited impatiently for the others to catch on.

"May we see the medallion?" asked Deborah. "It obviously holds the clues to unravel these bizarre events."

"Please, Jason, we must see Exhibit A," said Ricardo, wiping his spectacles on his napkin.

I reached into my pocket, pulled out the silver box containing the medallion, and with a dramatic flair, placed it on the table. Carefully prying open the box, I lifted the jewel-laden artifact by its golden chain, dangling it before their expectant gaze.

There was a moment's silence, broken by George. "Doesn't look worth killing for," he murmured. "Ten thousand sounds like a deal." Despite his cool demeanor, I detected George's excitement.

Ricardo and Deborah were more emphatic. "It's beautiful!" Deborah gasped.

"Amazing!" said Ricardo, his gray eyes flashing.

George inclined his head to get a closer look. "I've never seen anything like it," he said, "not even in a museum."

"May I touch it?" asked Ricardo, leaning over the table.

"Certainly, if you're careful. It appears to be very durable, but I wouldn't want to drop it. Pretty exceptional, don't you think?" A strange pride came over me, making me forget momentarily the danger and hardship which the medallion had already brought into my life.

Ricardo took the jewelled artifact, gently cradling it in his hands. "Isis!" he said softly, almost wistfully. "The supreme mother goddess of the ancients."

Deborah pushed her brown hair from her forehead. "The very embodiment of devotion," she added. "Divine, yet approachable. The Mediterranean world adored her."

"No doubt, it's extremely ancient," said Ricardo, stroking his mustache. "I'm no expert, but it may well date back to the days of the Egyptian pharaohs."

"That would make it at least twenty-five hundred years old," added Deborah.

"Possibly much older than that," said George, warming to the subject. "The Egyptian civilization goes back at least six thousand years, possibly more."

"The irony is that we have this beautiful piece," I said, "and no one to whom we can show it. After what I've been through already, I'm not about to flaunt it. But, you know, Ricardo, I feel as if I've stumbled upon one of your ancient relics...almost like the Grail, or something."

"Perhaps you're right," he said. "I feel as if I'm in the presence of something quite remarkable, even sacred."

"It must have some kind of unseen power," said Deborah, "if a man as wealthy as Bundy would be willing to kill for it."

"Perhaps it's a talisman of some sort," said Ricardo. "The ancient Egyptians were fascinated by objects which they believed possessed supernatural properties."

"I'm certain that explains Bundy's interest," George stated emphatically. "I've read that a lot of the financial insiders are Masons. They must have records of these things."

"Financial insiders?" Ricardo asked, stroking his silver

beard.

"You know," George said matter-of-factly. "The global elite. The international power brokers. The financial ruling establishment. It turns out that Bundy is a member of the Trilateral Commission."

"Oh really," said Ricardo. "I've been reading a great deal about these matters recently. Utterly fascinating, although rather disturbing."

"You know about this stuff?" I asked Ricardo, conscious that my mouth was hanging slightly open. Ricardo looked at me and nodded.

"Oh yes," Deborah said enthusiastically. "It makes perfect sense to me. It's obvious that a tiny minority holds most of the power in the economic and political world. I just read an article which estimated that in a few years 90% of all industrial and business activity world-wide will be in the hands of fewer than a thousand mega-corporations."

George glanced over at me, seeming to sense what was going through my mind. "Still think I'm nuts?" he asked, smiling faintly.

"The whole world's nuts," I answered, staring at Ricardo. I respected his judgment and hoped he would elaborate his opinions.

"How'd you get interested in this issue?" I asked him. "I thought you'd taken up gardening full time."

Ricardo took a sip of coffee, then cleared his throat. "It's very much tied up with that," he explained. "When we established our garden, Deborah and I wanted to use organic seeds, figuring that was the first step in a chemically free food chain." Ricardo gestured to his seed room. "We quickly discovered that the large petro-chemical companies were buying up all the small seed stores. They were introducing hybrid seeds — which they love — because they can be patented and don't reproduce effectively. As a result, farmers and gardeners are becoming dependent on the giant agribusiness establishment."

"So what you're saying," George volunteered, "is that these

chemical companies are gathering all the seed stores into their control, eliminating competition and cornering the global seed market."

"That's what it seems like," confirmed Deborah. "By buying up the seed inventories, and hybridizing the various strains, they effectively control agriculture at its roots — so to speak — making all the small growers dependent on them for seeds each year."

"One thing led to another," explained Ricardo, "and we discovered that this centralizing of power and influence in the hands of a relatively small number of multi-national corporations was happening in other fields as well, including global finance."

"That's amazing," I said. "But I don't see what it has to do with this." I pointed to the Egyptian artifact.

George picked up the medallion again, gazing carefully at the alien characters. "Probably a lot," he said. "At any rate, I'd certainly like to use some of these symbols in my oil paintings. They'd really make people scratch their heads." He took a pen from his pocket and began to copy one of the glyphs on a scrap of paper. Instantly, the glass of water in front of him broke.

"Jeeminy!" he shouted. "What the hell is going on?"

"Look at the picture!" exclaimed Deborah, pointing to a large, framed print of Kwan Yin, the Oriental mother goddess, which enjoyed an honored place on their wall. It had fallen sideways, dangling from its hook.

"Nothing like that's ever happened before," she said, getting up and straightening the picture.

"This is starting to give me the creeps," said George. He stood up and walked to the fireplace. One log, barely smoldering, remained from the previous evening's fire. Crumpling the scrap of paper on which he had scribbled the glyph, he tossed it on the log.

An odd blue smoke, a thin mist, curled immediately from the charred wood. It spiraled strangely, filling the room in a few seconds with a fog — real, yet seeming supernatural, so peculiar was its origin and color. All of us coughed and sputtered and Deborah ran to the door, flinging it ajar. The blue cloud condensed into a small, dense mass and floated outside, disappearing from view.

In that instant, the fire flamed and crackled violently, and the log exploded, splitting in two. Angry sparks flew against the grill.

George turned and walked back to the table, his face ashen. "By God, Jason," he said, trembling, "you've really got a beast by the tail."

"A sphinx, more likely," Ricardo muttered breathlessly.

"I knew this thing was important!" I said, feeling somehow vindicated by the bizarre phenomena. "It's got to go to the right people. We've got to learn more about the medallion. I mean, what exactly is its history? Could it be a relic of power, like the ancient Ark of the Covenant, which held the Ten Commandments?"

"Or the Spear of Longinus," said Ricardo, referring to the legendary spear belonging to the Roman soldier who pierced the side of Christ as he hung on the cross. According to certain arcane traditions, this "spear of destiny" was one of the most powerful of earthly talismans, as well as one of the most sacred.

"I think you're right," Ricardo continued. "We ought to get to the bottom of this and determine just what kind of a mess you've gotten yourself into." He looked at me seriously.

"But how?" said George. "Who can you turn to that you trust? I know you people are into King Arthur and the Holy Grail, and all that stuff. But I'm afraid I'm not on close terms with any enlightened beings, present company excepted."

"I think I know just the person who can help us," Ricardo said, his eyes shining. He looked at Deborah and she nodded.

"Brother Arthur," they said, simultaneously.

"Brother Arthur!" George exclaimed. He could tell that Ricardo and Deborah were not joking. "Well, maybe this is the Round Table after all." He rubbed his hands on the curved, wooden side of the circular breakfast table. "I need more coffee to keep up with you people," he said, pouring himself a fresh cup from the ceramic pitcher. "In the meantime, you can call me Lancelot."

Chapter Six
BROTHER ARTHUR
"Truth is a language with no accent." E.J.M.

For the next hour we sifted options. George had to return to Marin County. He would speak to Melissa, and we agreed that either he or his wife, Jenny, should call Ricardo at least every other day to communicate developments or plans. Calls would be from pay phones, to avoid the risk of phone taps.

As George stood at his car, preparing to set off, I removed my L.T.A. paycheck from my wallet, endorsed it payable to Melissa, and handed it to him. "Give this to Melissa," I said. "Just because I'm unemployed doesn't mean I'm a flake."

George and I hugged, then he started down the shadowy driveway. As Ricardo, Deborah and I watched him go, the sound of a low-flying helicopter snared our attention.

"Must be a drug helicopter," said Deborah. "They fly around here looking for marijuana in the woods." I was well aware that pot was a big cash crop in Mendocino county. We strained to catch a glimpse of the craft and were rewarded when it appeared for several seconds through a break in the trees.

"That doesn't look like a police 'copter, or the ones the drug teams use," said Ricardo. "They have clear markings."

"That one's totally black, with no markings," I said, the concern evident in my voice. "There's more and more of that going on. I've seen them over the hills in Marin and I understand you can see them all over California. No one I've talked to seems to know who they belong to."

"My understanding," said Ricardo, "is that all helicopters, as well as airplanes, must have clear identifying markings. That would make this type illegal."

"Or above the law," said Deborah.

"Not a very comforting thought," I sighed, "especially since they seem to be so interested in your house." The chopper had reversed direction and flew over the Schuller home a second time.

"Well, my friend," Ricardo said, putting his hand on my shoulder. "I don't think you should let the soles of your feet gather any dust. Let's see if we can meet with Brother Arthur today." He disappeared into the house to make a phone call, and minutes later the two of us were in his old white pickup truck, heading toward town.

Ricardo had often told me about Brother Arthur and I had long wanted to meet him. Brother Arthur was a priest of the Russian Orthodox Church and served in a small chapel in Mendocino. He was born in Russia, and had escaped the communists as a young boy. Most of his family had been killed or sent to the work camps.

By a twist of fate, he had gone to Greece where he lived for several years before traveling extensively in the Near East and the Orient. His journeys took him to virtually every country in the world. He became fluent in nearly a dozen languages, and, while still a young man, became a Jesuit priest in Italy. He served in the Vatican, and Ricardo told me that he had been so admired for his scholarship and brilliant mind that he had gained access to the Vatican archives, containing some of the most extraordinary writings extant upon earth, most of them carefully withheld from the public.

At a critical point in his life, Brother Arthur had left the Roman Catholic fold, renouncing his Jesuit allegiance, and had continued his travels. He had for several years lived the contemplative life of a monk in a Japanese Zen monastery before finally coming to America, where he married a young woman whom he knew to have terminal leukemia. His wife died within a year, and for three years following, Arthur became a recluse, secluded in a cabin in the Canadian Rockies.

Returning to the United States, Arthur once again entered the monastic world, this time in the church of his parents. Ricardo considered Arthur to be by far the most erudite and enlightened person he had ever known — possibly of the spiritual stature of the unknown man who had so mysteriously come to our aid on the Cornwall cliffs.

After a pleasant drive, we arrived at a quaint little Russian Orthodox chapel set amidst the luxurious fields and forests of Mendocino. As we got out of Ricardo's truck, a bearded man in a simple black cloak stepped vigorously towards us. I knew it was Brother Arthur.

"Ricardo, my friend," the man said, extending his hand in greeting. "How glad I am to see you. And this must be Jason." He turned to me, smiling, and shook my hand. His grip was strong and he held my hands for several seconds, looking searchingly into my eyes. He appeared to be about fifty, but I knew from his remarkable biography that he must be at least seventy. His white hair was full and thick, matching exactly the white of his trim beard; he showed no signs of balding. His eyes were a piercing blue, his forehead broad. His presence radiated vitality, and he gave me the overall impression of controlled power.

"Thank you so much, Brother Arthur," said Ricardo, as we walked inside the rustic chapel, "for allowing us to see you at such short notice. But, I believe you can shed light on some important matters. I feel certain we won't be wasting your time."

"Not at all, not at all," Brother Arthur said graciously. "I consider it a privilege...and my curiosity is acutely aroused. I have a hunch we'll be dealing with matters at the very heart of goings-on these days. 'Core issues,' as they say. One might almost say I've been expecting you." He had a mild accent, vaguely European, no particular foreign idiom seeming to dominate. His command of English was impeccable.

The kind priest ushered us into his small study, gesturing toward a couple of old leather armchairs to one side of a brown desk. The desk was bare save for a small framed print of Raphael's "Transfigured Christ." He served us some ice tea, then sat down in a leather chair identical to ours.

We exchanged pleasantries, and I felt completely at ease in his presence. The atmosphere of his study was vitalized, almost electric. The only wall surface not devoted to books, many quite old, was a small alcove in which he had created a tiny altar or shrine.

Ensconced upon the altar was a rosewood carving of the Madonna in an attitude of blessing. To one side was a small framed picture of the Archangel Michael, slaying the dragon. On the other side was an object that momentarily caused my heart to pound. It was a miniature figurine — apparently of painted ceramic or plaster — of the winged Isis, kneeling with outstretched wings, a solar disc behind her head. It was nearly the identical pose of the Isis on the medallion I had discovered. I sensed immediately that an unseen hand had guided us to the right person.

Brother Arthur held me captive with his gaze. "I understand, Jason," he said, "that your situation is urgent. Feel free to confide in me; I'll do my utmost to be of assistance." There was a quality in Arthur's voice and manner I could only describe as compassionate. And I was impressed with a rare feature of character he seemed to possess: remarkable self-assurance combined with genuine humility.

"Thank you, Brother Arthur. I don't know where to begin. So much has happened in the last day and a half, it's as if I've compressed years of experience into a few hours."

"Difficult, to be sure," said Arthur. "Do persevere. Those periods in our life in which we have most to endure are those which bear the ripest fruit. Can you give details?"

"I may as well get right to the point. It seems that time's running out. I've become a fugitive...that is, I've gone into hiding. You see, there's been an attempt on my life."

"Why's that, may I ask? Have you committed a crime?"

"Not one that I'm aware of," I said, grinning painfully. The thought of the Pharaoh's Curse occurred to me again. The discomfort I felt was surely visible on my face. "At least not in this lifetime."

"You believe in reincarnation, then?" asked Brother Arthur.

"It's always made sense to me. And I've had many strong feelings that I've lived before. I feel a connection to several ancient cultures, and a geographic attraction to certain parts of the earth. I'm also keenly interested in history."

"In particular, with what areas of the earth, and with what ancient cultures do you feel a kinship?"

"Ancient Egypt, Greece, Italy, Peru and the lost Mayan civilization of Yucatan," I answered without hesitation.

"Most interesting," Arthur commented. He gave me the impression of listening carefully, yet simultaneously living with great intensity in a thought world all his own. He appeared to possess awesome powers of concentration. "Tell me more."

I then described how I came to find the strange medallion, and the incidents that led to our arrival at his church. Overcoming some lingering hesitation, I pulled the silver box out of my pocket, opened it, and handed the ancient artifact to the old priest. "Can you help me, Brother Arthur? What is it that I've found?"

Brother Arthur held the piece lovingly, gently moving his fingers over the dazzling jewels and ancient gold. His hands began to tremble. Then, surprisingly, his eyes became wet. A hush fell over us, and an otherworldly aura filled the room. Anticipation thrilled every fiber of my mind and body.

Arthur closed his eyes for a moment, as if in silent prayer. "Ah, most blessed day," he said softly, almost under his breath. "Most sacred and auspicious day."

He opened his eyes and stared at me. "You, my son," he said, "are fortunate indeed. Your destiny has given you a most unusual task, yet truly a difficult one."

I could barely contain my curiosity. "What do you mean,

Brother Arthur? I still don't understand what I've found."

"More probably, Jason, it has found you." Brother Arthur paused, caressing the medallion in both his hands, as if it were some precious, living thing. "This artifact is the legendary Medallion of Isis, one of the most sublime treasures of the ancient world." He looked at us each in turn — a penetrating gaze — as if to size up our appreciation of his revelation.

"As you both have surmised, its value and importance vastly exceed mere monetary considerations. This is the greatest talisman of the wondrous Egyptian epoch, which spanned more than seven thousand years and reached a spiritual glory of which our century has barely an inkling. This sacred amulet is, in a very real sense, the repository of that lost glory. And though spiritual in essence, it contains a concentrated force which, if knowingly manipulated, gives the holder awesome power in the world of physical reality."

Ricardo and I looked at each other. I could tell that he, too, was electrified by Arthur's words. "What does that mean exactly?" Ricardo asked, barely able to suppress his excitement.

"It means many things," said Arthur, abruptly standing up. He walked to the only window in his study and dramatically closed it. Then he opened the door through which we had entered and peered down both ends of the corridor. Apparently satisfied, he closed and locked the door. "Please understand that we must now cross a threshold."

The tension was almost too much for me to bear. "What do you mean?" I asked. "What kind of a threshold?"

He stared at me again with the gaze of an ancient hierophant, penetrating beneath pretentious facades, sizing up the worthiness of one's soul.

"We must draw a line in the sand," continued Arthur. "From this moment on, your lives will never be the same. It appears that you, Jason, have little choice in the matter, having elected, at least subconsciously, to put yourself through the coming ordeals." I swallowed hard, not thrilled about the prospect of yet more hardships.

"But you, Ricardo," Arthur continued, "have the opportunity to leave now, if you choose. If you elect to stay and participate in our conversation, you will be obliged to carry a heavy responsibility in this, the final hour of our present global era. Naturally, with that responsibility comes opportunity. What is your decision?"

Ricardo blinked, then looked at me for a long moment. He closed his eyes, deep in thought, then smiled faintly. "It looks as if we're all in this together," he sighed. I took a deep breath, then exhaled noisily. Brother Arthur's countenance glowed brightly.

"Very well, then," he said. "Destiny has set the stage. I pray we live to see the entire play." He placed the medallion next to the Isis figurine and lit a votive candle. The candle flickered for an instant, threatened by a draft — perhaps from beneath the door — then steadied. A shadow crossed Arthur's imperturbable features. He hovered momentarily by the tiny shrine, then sat down.

Chapter Seven
SECRETS OF THE MEDALLION
"Those who talk with God
are most worth listening to." E.J.M.

"According to ancient tradition," Arthur began, "the Isis Medallion gives the one or ones who can tap its potency the power to exert dominion over material substance." Arthur paused to look at us.

"Dominion over material substance?" I shook my head incredulously. "That sounds like something from fantasy, or maybe science fiction."

Arthur was silent for a moment. "Such is the legend," he again affirmed. "Allow yourselves to imagine, if you will, that the legend is true. Do you realize what this would mean?"

Ricardo and I stared at each other. "Well, obviously," I said, somewhat hesitantly, "that would confer tremendous spiritual and material leverage. I suppose you could then do just about anything."

Ricardo thought a moment. "It would give a person the potential for mastering the physical universe," he said, his eyes shining.

Arthur looked at us intently, then at the relic. "Its potential is limitless. It contains many secrets, among them the most profound mysteries of life and existence. Down the ages, few have concerned themselves with the deeper mysteries of the medallion. Historically, it has been sought by those seeking temporal power and advantage over their fellow men."

"You mean political and financial power?" I asked.

"I mean," said Arthur, "that the medallion transmits the power with which to influence world destiny. The bearer of the medallion has the potential to actually achieve world dominion. Such, at least, is the legend."

"Do you believe the legend?" I asked, staggered by the implications of his words.

"Not a blind belief, mind you. The historical facts support it."

"You must know the history, then," said Ricardo. "Can you tell us?"

Arthur paused for a moment, as if considering how much he ought to reveal. "It's a long story," he said, "though much remains hidden. I'll share what I know.

"Let me say at the outset that what passes today as conventional history is a mere skeleton, a distorted caricature, of the true history of the earth, the natural world and humanity. There are horrendous errors...monstrous mis-directions...in the modern worldview. Fortunately, truth, like oil, no matter how deeply submerged, will eventually rise to the surface. In the near future, the facts will once again see the light of day.

"Five thousand years ago, as Egyptian civilization approached its zenith, a high priest-initiate, Thoth by name, commissioned the finest jewelers of Egypt to strike a medallion of unparalleled beauty, a medallion in honor of the glorious Isis, mother Goddess of the ancient world. Truth to tell, it was Isis herself who commissioned the work, but modern minds can scarcely grasp the meaning of such words.

"After the medallion was struck, the most beautiful jewels in the pharaoh's vast treasure hoards were imbedded into the precious metal. Each is itself a jewel of power as well as beauty. These stones have been charged with a force not entirely of this earth. This ancient art, now lost, was used to impregnate jewels of great beauty with a quality of energy that could heal, inspire and influence. The amulet received the blessing of the most learned and spiritually advanced priests and priestesses of that day.

"The Goddess Isis herself — who, I assure you, is not a product of mythic imagination, but a cosmic Personality of incalculable greatness — gave her blessing to the talisman. I believe one reason she caused it to be created — through the inspired agency of the Adept, Thoth — was that she hoped its influence would help avert the impending spiritual decline of the Egyptian mysteries. The decline occurred nonetheless. Of course, this process lasted thousands of years."

Arthur began to point out the various glyphs and characters embossed and engraved upon the mysterious artifact. "The highest wisdom of antiquity went into the crafting of this relic. There are twenty-two major symbols appearing here, as well as other minor symbols. Most of them you will not find in any historical text surviving from ancient Egypt. These were not for the profane, and usually were not even written on the temple walls. These glyphs, as well as having incredible power for those who can employ them magically, spell out the greatest secret of the ancient world."

"What's that?" I asked.

"Theogeny," answered Arthur.

"Theogeny?" both Ricardo and I asked, bewildered.

"In other words," said Arthur, "the sacred and exceedingly controversial idea that the seed of the Gods...the Divine Spark...is planted within each human soul. By cultivating this God-seed, a man or woman may become divine."

"Is that really so mysterious?" asked Ricardo.

"Perhaps not to the two of you, who have been involved in these more esoteric fields for years. But it is the most revolutionary idea the world has ever known.

"In ancient times," continued Arthur, "the temples of wisdom jealously guarded this concept from the uninitiated. Hermes Trismegistus, in his *Divine Hermetica,* gave this knowledge to the world in written form. Fortunately, some of these ancient manuscripts survived the great fire at the Library of Alexandria two thousand years ago, in which most of the vast learning of antiquity went up in smoke. During the Renaissance, Marsilio Ficino, the court scholar-philosopher of Cosimo de' Medici, translated these ancient writings. When first printed in Florence in 1471, the *Hermetica* changed forever the Western world. The New Age, as some now call it, actually began at that time."

"So what you're saying," I said, "is that even though some of us take these ideas for granted, in the larger scope of history they're still almost hot off the papyrus, so to speak."

"Exactly," nodded Arthur.

"And all these ideas," said Ricardo, "are graphically depicted in the symbolism inscribed on the medallion."

"Exactly," repeated Arthur. He paused a moment, then continued. "By meditating upon the symbolic language of the medallion, one may awaken his intuitive and visionary faculties, leading ultimately to the birth of subtle, spiritual perceptions and abilities.

"Look here," he said, pointing to the reverse side of the medallion, which displayed the solar disc — the interlocking circles forming the six-petalled flower design at its heart — and the seven rays streaming from the sun, a hand at the end of each ray. Beneath each ray was a glyph or symbol. "The sun represents God, or the Divine World. The design at its center is the mystic Flower of Life, embodying the mystery of creation. The solar rays represent emanations of the divine, which have the power to completely transform human life. One may think of them as divine laws or principles. When one applies these laws, he or she can achieve perfection in the areas of life to which they correspond."

"Can you explain in more detail?" I asked. "I mean, what exactly are the laws which the solar rays represent?"

"Of course," Arthur nodded. "They may be expressed as follows. The Law of Reciprocity. The Law of Supply. The Law of Celestial Guidance. The Law of Right Relationships. The Law of Conscious Evolution. The Law of Spiritual Freedom, and the Law of Universal Oneness." Arthur paused and stared at each of us in turn. "Application of each of these principles illuminates an area of human life, leading eventually to self-mastery."

Arthur gazed intently at the medallion, appearing to gain inspiration from the dazzling artifact.

"The deepest secrets of life," he persisted, "truly the most profound mysteries, are encoded upon this relic. It is an inspired scripture in metal and jewels. Down the ages, most who have coveted it have sought worldly power. Such is true today. Fools and tyrants seek power over others; the wise seek power over themselves. Thus, the deepest secret of the medallion remains hidden." Arthur hesitated a moment, lost momentarily in his own private contemplations. His face and eyes shone with intense brilliance.

"The deepest secret of the medallion," Ricardo said, a far away look in his eyes. "Hmmn...that sounds intriguing, almost romantic."

"Won't you tell us the deepest secret?" I asked, conscious of how naive my question must have sounded.

"Patience, Jason," said Arthur. "That's something you must intuit through your own inner activity. Suffice it to say that the symbolism of the medallion in its entirety points to one of the greatest of celestial truths. This is the medallion's ultimate message, its deepest secret." He paused, apparently gathering his thoughts.

"I won't go into details," Arthur continued, picking up his narrative, "of the medallion's checkered history in ancient Egypt, except to note that it changed hands often over the centuries.

"As Egypt's greatness was eclipsed by other Mediterranean civilizations, the relic was taken from that land. It came into the hands of Alexander the Great when, during his exploits, he conquered Egypt and founded the great learning center at Alexandria. As you know, he went on to conquer most of the known world."

"Wasn't Alexander little more than a glorified general?" Ricardo asked.

"He was far more than that," Arthur answered. "Alexander was a pupil of Aristotle, himself a high initiate of the Mysteries and perhaps the greatest of Greek philosophers. Alexander had an incredibly developed will. Imagine a man of such magnetism, energy, and will power that the gods themselves would pause in their affairs to admire him. Such a man was Alexander. His conquests were meant to serve a spiritual purpose. It was Alexander's task to carry the torch of Greek culture, idealism, art and learning throughout the Mediterranean and Asiatic world.

"Greek — that is, Hellenic or Hellenistic — culture was among the most beautiful and inspired that the world has ever known. We owe our idea of the value and sanctity of the individual to that era.

"You see, among the higher spiritual beings whose task it is to guide mankind, plans are laid centuries, even millennia, in advance of their outworking on earth. Thus, Alexander's mission was to create a common universal culture from Rome to India in advance of the incarnation of the Being known to our world today as the Christ. Alexander was only partially successful, due in large part to the excesses and shortcomings of his own otherwise remarkable personality." Arthur paused, peering deeply into our eyes, as if to ascertain the extent of our comprehension.

"Did Alexander appreciate the significance of the medallion?" I asked.

"To some extent," answered Arthur, "I believe he did. He also intimated its higher meaning, but was unable to hold fast to that more exalted vision.

"At Alexander's death, the medallion was taken by one of his generals to Rome. This coincided with the rapid ascent of Rome to world prominence and dominion. Many of the Roman emperors were aware of the Egyptian relic, but few had more than a vague notion of its importance. Julius Caesar is said to have owned it briefly.

"After the collapse of Roman civilization, the medallion remained in Europe for many centuries in the possession of the Roman Church, headquartered in the Vatican. Charlemagne tried to acquire it and may have succeeded for a brief time. Of this I'm not certain."

"Isn't it interesting," I interjected, "that during the time you say the Vatican had it, the established Church grew to have incredible power and influence throughout Europe."

"Interesting," responded Arthur, "and I think more than coincidental. "Through a series of unusual events," he continued, "the medallion was given to Ferdinand and Isabella of

Spain. Subsequently, it was brought to the New World by Jesuit priests, following in the wake of the Conquistadors.

"A certain Jesuit, Dante by name, intuited the higher meaning and importance of the medallion. Despite his allegiance to the Christian faith, he distrusted the intentions of certain of his superiors, who he felt would abuse the medallion's power for selfish purpose."

Arthur paused and looked at me strangely. I had a peculiar feeling that he could perceive my thoughts. "Dante was deeply touched," he continued, "by the gentleness and innate spirituality of the Mayan people in the Yucatan peninsula. He conceived the idea of giving them the medallion, thus foiling the plans of his superiors. He failed in his effort and his intentions were exposed. Consequently, he was put to death by his brother monks."

"It hardly seems possible," I said, "given the strict Jesuit training and discipline, that the monk would even think of such a bold plan."

"True. But it appears, from independent spiritual research that I have done, that the idealistic Dante had been incarnated in both the Egyptian and Mayan civilizations at different periods. In his Egyptian incarnation, he had come into direct contact with the talisman. This accounted for his intuition regarding its importance."

When Arthur spoke of "independent spiritual research," it occurred to me that he must have possessed a highly developed clairvoyance which enabled him to engage in direct research of the so-called "akashic records," the memory of nature, recorded in light upon the sensitive spiritual ether that interpenetrated our physical dimension. I had read of others who had developed this type of exact clairvoyance. Apparently Rudolf Steiner, the Austrian spiritual scientist, possessed it to a remarkable extent. Edgar Cayce, the American trance medium, had access to these same records in an unconscious state.

Brother Arthur continued his outline history. "The Jesuits returned the medallion to Spain, where Philip II entrusted the amulet to a nobleman who was to play an important role in the organizing of the Spanish Armada. He was a ship's captain on that fateful voyage to England in 1588.

"As you know, a great storm arose and destroyed most of the Armada before it met the English navy. The nobleman's ship sank and he was rescued, near death, by the vessel which Sir Francis Drake commanded. The dying nobleman entrusted the medallion to Drake. It is remarkably synchronistic that the defeat of the Armada — and the passing of the medallion into English control — signalled the dawn of that era when Spain would fall into decline, while England took center stage in the drama of world history."

"Sir Francis Drake!" I cried out, the light going on in my mind. "That's what the initials S.F.D. mean!"

Brother Arthur smiled. "You're catching on," he said.

"So Drake obviously brought it with him to the New World," Ricardo commented. "And it's well known that he visited the San Francisco Bay area, spending time in what is today Marin County."

"How did he lose it?" I asked. "Didn't he appreciate its value?"

"He certainly recognized its historical value, but not its power as a talisman," answered Arthur, folding his hands together on the desk. "Nevertheless, he must have been deeply chagrined at its disappearance. Apparently, some of the Indians of the Bay Area stole the relic. To them it was a prized possession, but they, too, were ignorant of its extraordinary mystical properties.

"When the Spanish padres entered the area of what is today Marin County, the Indians buried the medallion. They had hoped to retrieve it, of course, but were soon subjugated by the Spaniards. The medallion's exact location remained a secret. The Spanish Catholics, particularly the Jesuits, had reason to believe that the medallion was close by, yet they were unable to find it.

"My personal conviction," the burly monk explained, "is

that it was necessary for the medallion to remain hidden for several centuries, as we entered the modern age of scientific materialism. Maybe the great Lady whom the treasured relic honors," Arthur gestured toward the Isis figurine, "saw to it that the amulet was lost. Now a historical era comes to a close and a new epoch dawns. Perhaps the medallion shall once more play a role in world events."

Ricardo's eyes burned with enthusiasm. "It's remarkable," he said, "that during the time the medallion was buried beneath California soil, this region became the vanguard for so much cultural change."

"The whole story is absolutely amazing!" I said. "But why should I be the one to stumble upon it?"

Arthur smiled enigmatically. "Undoubtedly," he said, "you'll one day know."

"How did you learn of the medallion's past?" Ricardo asked.

Arthur turned the shining relic over in his hands. "I learned of the medallion first as a Jesuit, but primarily through the unusual access I had as one of the chief scholars and researchers in the Vatican archives. I became privy to information of which barely a handful of people in the world are aware."

I shook my head wonderingly at Arthur's strange and fascinating narrative. "I can now appreciate," I said, "why there are people and groups out there who would do anything to get their hands on the medallion. But how do you suppose Ulysses Bundy recognized it?"

"From what I know of Bundy," Arthur answered, "and the occult, financial group of which he is an important member, it does not surprise me. They too have secret historical records dating back to the time of the Egyptian mystery schools. Bundy is a high-level Mason and must have studied this arcane lore."

"That bastard!" I said. "Oh, excuse my language." I turned a little red. An oath of that kind seemed inappropriate in Arthur's dignified presence.

"Perfectly understandable sentiments," said Arthur, his face impassive. We remained silent for several minutes. Arthur was studying the medallion and seemed to be impervious to our presence. He looked up abruptly and his laser stare cut through me.

"There's one more thing I must tell you, Jason. It's obviously your destiny to have stumbled upon the medallion. Beware. Most of those down the centuries who have possessed the talisman have died a violent death." He paused for a moment, letting the impact of his words hit home.

"So long as you carry it," he continued, "your life will be tumultuous. At the same time, the potential for growth is unparalleled." Before I could respond to Arthur's foreboding declarations, we were brought to our feet by a loud drone above the chapel.

"Helicopters!" Ricardo exclaimed, alarm in his voice.

"Gentlemen," said Brother Arthur, picking up the medallion and escorting us to the door of his study, "it seems someone is interested in your whereabouts."

"Oh, God," I moaned. "My mother used to tell me I had a nose for trouble. What'll I do now?" Arthur handed me the jewelled pendant, which he had placed in the silver box.

"Have you thought of asking her?" he queried.

"Ask my mother!" I said, bewildered. "I don't understand."

"*The* Mother," said Arthur, glancing at the medallion. "The Divine Mother." As we walked out to Ricardo's truck, I uttered a desperate prayer to the celestial powers for guidance and protection.

Before we reached Ricardo's white pickup, a dusty blue car skidded to a halt beside us. Out jumped Deborah Schuller, looking shaken and alarmed.

"You all right, dear?" Ricardo asked. "You look as if you've wandered into the C.I.A.'s marijuana patch."

"I just got a call from Jenny Fort. They picked up George when he arrived home, searched him, and found the check you gave him, Jason. They know you're alive, and they think you're here in Mendocino. You can't come back with us. These damn helicopters are some kind of elite surveillance. You've got to get away. A long way away!"

For a moment we stood there, paralyzed. "Oh God, where can I go?" I said. "Where will I hide?"

"Perhaps it's time you get some religion," Arthur said, taking hold of my arm.

"What do you mean?" I asked, perplexed.

"I mean, I think you'd look great as a Russian Orthodox monk, don't you?"

I grasped Arthur's thought as he nudged me back toward the chapel. "That sounds like a plan!" I shouted, running up the sanctuary steps. The bizarre twist of events made me smile. "As long as I don't have to take a vow of celibacy," I said under my breath. "Melissa would never approve."

I ran into the chapel behind Arthur, with Ricardo and Deborah at our heels.

Chapter Eight
PARTING OF THE WAYS

"If you stop at nothing, nothing can stop you." E.J.M.

Within the hour I had metamorphosed. Brother Arthur gave me a crew cut and I shampooed blond hair-color into what remained of my hair. He supplied me with a pair of black spectacles with clear glass lenses. In my black robe, I looked the part of a young, intellectual monk.

"This will help," said Arthur, "but you must still leave the area without delay."

"Where will I go?" I asked, looking for guidance.

"Listen to your heart," advised Brother Arthur. "Follow your intuition." In that instant, a picture came to mind of an enormous expanse of semi-tropical jungle. It might have been any jungle region in the world except for the ancient pyramids that rose above the trees. Mayan pyramids.

"I'm going to leave the country," I announced. "I'm going to Mexico."

"Mexico?" Ricardo and Deborah asked together. I nodded affirmatively, surprised at my own sudden conviction as to the rightness of my choice.

"Yucatan, to be exact." The abrupt intuition left no room for doubt.

"And you should leave not later than tomorrow," Arthur said. "If necessary, I'll drive you to the border myself."

"I was leaving for Mexico next week," said Ricardo, "on a business trip. Perhaps I can meet you there."

"But I can't bear to leave without seeing Melissa and Angelina at least one more time," I said, feelings for my family pushing aside more reasonable judgment.

"Can you risk it, Jason?" Deborah asked painfully. "Wouldn't that jeopardize everything?"

"There may yet be a way," Brother Arthur said, a faint smile at the corners of his mouth. "After all...I've spent most of my life in the miracle business."

The four of us huddled together, talking quietly. Minutes later, Deborah and Ricardo hurried from the chapel and drove away, each going separate ways. I spent the remainder of the day in a small room on one wing of the chapel, not far from Brother Arthur's study. I conversed with him briefly, but spent most of my time brooding over my plans and the revelations of that morning.

In the late afternoon, there came a soft tapping at my door. "Come in," I whispered, supposing it to be Arthur. However, a stranger entered, dressed in the black of the Russian Orthodox order. Excepting Arthur, he was the first monk I had met that day. He was tall and thin, with a hungry, discontented look. His thin, aquiline nose had obviously once been broken, and his nostrils seemed too large for the rest of his face. There was a brilliance in his eyes, almost a fierceness. It was the light of high intelligence, I thought to myself, but not of wisdom.

"Hello there," I said awkwardly.

"And who might you be?" he asked. "I was not aware of any new brothers at the chapel."

"I...well, I'm a friend of Arthur's," I stammered. "Just visiting for the evening."

"Oh really?" The man's voice was unpleasant. Condescending. "A stowaway on our voyage through life. How quaint. You seem uncomfortable in your new outfit." He gestured at my robe. "Are you hiding from something?" I didn't know whether to lie, or admit that I was an imposter in the monk's garb.

"I'm just, uh, trying them on. I'm considering entering the priesthood, and on a whim, Brother Arthur let me wear the robe. Sort of silly, I suppose. I didn't mean to offend anyone."

"Not at all," the man laughed. "Life is full of masquerades and pretense." He stepped forward and straightened the heavy cross hanging at my chest. "What's your name?"

Again I hesitated, not having rehearsed my new role as a fugitive. "Uh...Jay," I said. "Actually Jason, but sometimes people call me Jay."

"How nice to be given a bird's name," the unpleasant monk continued. "My name is Reynard. A name sometimes given to foxes." Something about his expression was cruel. "Pleased to meet you," he said. We shook hands briefly.

The wood of the hall floor creaked outside the door and, seconds later, Brother Arthur entered. He stared at Brother Reynard and I thought I detected an uncharacteristic hint of displeasure in his countenance. "Greetings, Reynard," he said, regaining his serenity. "I see you've discovered our fugitive."

"Why yes, Arthur," Reynard said, coldness in his voice. "I've often told you, you should have entered the field of espionage. Intrigue simply becomes you."

"My friend Jason has stumbled upon a bit of hard luck and I'm helping him out...in accordance with our priestly vocation. I trust you'll be discreet." He gave Reynard a piercing look.

"You have my word, Arthur. Trouble with the law, I presume?"

"Possibly. But I'm sure the young man is innocent. I'm giving him shelter for the night and he will leave tomorrow."

"But of course, of course," said Reynard, the trace of a smile on his lips. "Innocent until proven guilty. Well, if I may be of any assistance, don't hesitate to ask." He bowed slightly and left the room. The meeting made me uncomfortable and I spoke to Arthur about it. He briefly told me numerous peculiar facts about Reynard, then left me on my own for the remainder of the evening.

I spent that night mulling over the improbable sequence of events that had brought me to the Russian Orthodox chapel. Meditating upon the unfolding pattern of my life, I drifted into a mystical revery, seeking insight and inspiration. Deep in prayer, I asked the guiding spiritual powers to direct my footsteps. In a flight of inspired fantasy, I pleaded my case before a celestial court of seraphic beings and begged for my family's protection. I fell asleep, clutching the Isis Medallion tightly in my hands.

The next day was Sunday, and people began arriving at nine-thirty for the weekly chapel service. Arthur had given me strict orders to stay hidden. Gazing discreetly through a small window in the room where I had spent the night, I watched people drive into the parking lot.

The small parking area filled rapidly. Ricardo and Deborah pulled up, dressed like yuppies out for a night on the town. It wasn't common for them to attend a service; they preferred to keep their spiritual observances private.

An old, black Mercedes rolled in, and I laughed aloud. Out stepped Jenny Fort, followed by Melissa and Angelina, gaily dressed. I remained hidden in the shadows of my room, silly with happiness.

Minutes later, the organ's peal signalled the start of the Mass. There came a gentle knock at my door. I hesitated, then watched as someone turned the handle from the other side. It

was Brother Arthur, robed in vestments, holding a teddy bear.
"Aren't you leading the Mass?" I asked.

"I am, but first I must introduce you to a friend." I waited
curiously as he motioned someone to enter. My heart leaped
when I saw the familiar violet skirt of Melissa. Angelina was
in her arms, clutching a lollipop. When she saw me, Melissa
covered her mouth to keep from laughing. Despite her momen-
tary mirth, her eyes revealed weariness and pain. She appeared
to have lost several pounds from her already slender frame.

"Should've brought my camera," Melissa said softly.

"We can't leave any evidence," I said, taking her into my
arms.

"I'll leave the three of you," said Arthur, handing the teddy
bear to Angelina, "and be back when I've done my priestly
duties. You should be safe here, but make no noise." He winked
at Angelina, then disappeared through the door.

Melissa and I tenderly embraced. She told me how Deborah
had driven all the way to Marin, to the home of a mutual
friend, who had then gone to see Melissa and Jenny. Plans
were made for the two of them to drive up for the service. The
miracle was made possible thanks to Deborah's sacrificing five
hours of driving time, thereby avoiding phone conversations.

It took a few minutes for Angelina to get used to my new
look, but soon she was playing beside me and in my arms.
Melissa told me that George had been detained, questioned,
then released. He had told his questioners that he had driven
me as far as Mendocino, and that I wanted to go to Canada
or Alaska — that I was behaving strangely, and had apparently
snapped. George felt certain his interrogators weren't police,
but some special agents, perhaps C.I.A.

I told Melissa of my decision to go to Mexico, to Yucatan.
Then a crazy idea popped into my mind. "Why don't you meet
me there?" I asked her. "At the pyramid in Chichén Itzá! We'll
make a date!"

"Oh, God," she said, "it's totally lunatic, but I think we
should try. It's just like us to do something wild like this."

The sounds of the organ and the solemn Mass resonated above us. "Just like college," I said, repeating our private joke. We held each other tightly. Despite the awkward situation — or perhaps in part because of it — passionate feelings began to stir. We laughed at the comic absurdity of our circumstances.

Melissa poked me in the ribs, smiling impishly. "I always knew you'd make a lousy monk," she teased.

"Too many sacrifices," I chuckled. "I could more easily turn lead to gold than sublimate my sexuality."

"You'd better start praying and meditating a lot more earnestly," Melissa said, half-playfully.

"All I've done is pray ever since you left," I said, becoming somber despite my efforts.

Melissa winced and her eyes became watery. "Me too," she sighed, leaning her head on mine. "The past two days have been awful."

Neither of us dared speak the dreadful thought lurking in our minds, each wondering if this was the last time we'd ever be together as a family. Melissa began softly to hum a lullaby, the one she'd sung so often to Angelina, even while she carried her before birth. Tears filled my eyes. All at once I knew that my world was coming to an end.

The sounds from above told us the Mass had ended. We heard a soft tap at the door. The handle turned and Brother Arthur entered, his finger to his mouth. It was time to go. Melissa and I held each other in one last embrace. I picked up Angelina and kissed her, whispering my love.

"Remember," I said to Melissa. "Chichén Itzá, September 23rd...the Autumn Equinox...at the pyramid." I clenched my teeth to keep from crying.

Melissa smiled bravely. "No way I'd miss it...not for the world." She reached into her purse and handed me a small bag containing some of my personal belongings. Then she gave me my passport. "You'll be needing this...I love you." She gave me a long look from the depths of her soul — a look I would never forget. I smiled at Angelina, and all the love of my heart streamed from my eyes. My love would always surround her. Forever!

"I want to stay with daddy," she said.

"I'll be home soon, love," I whispered. "Don't you worry. Daddy loves you, treasure girl." I wiped the tears from my eyes. Brother Arthur took Melissa by the arm and nudged her through the door. We shared a last, searching glance — a glance that held a life of hopes, memories, love and fear. Then they were gone.

Peering from the tiny window, I saw them walk out into the parking lot and join Ricardo and Deborah. Brother Arthur spoke with them a moment. An ominous, black car pulled into the chapel lot and four men, dressed in black, stepped out. They looked more like secret servicemen than Sunday worshippers. Brother Arthur smiled politely, then turned to walk away.

"May we have a word with you, Father?" one of the men in black asked.

"Not just now," Arthur answered. "A parishioner needs me." He hustled into the chapel.

The men in black began to question Melissa, Jenny, Ricardo and Deborah. I prayed Angelina wouldn't reveal my presence. The conversation was indistinct, but I heard very clearly the words, "to Canada."

Brother Arthur appeared at the door. I seized the brown rucksack Ricardo had given me, catching a final, forlorn glimpse of the parking lot. We hurried down the darkened corridor and out the back of the chapel. Moments later, I was sprawled on the floor of Arthur's mini-van. We pulled onto the main road, going south. Destination — Mexico!

Chapter Nine
THE ESCAPE

"One does not become enlightened by imagining figures
of light, but by making the darkness conscious."
—Carl Jung

Arthur drove as if late to his own wedding, and by sunset we were crossing the Mojave desert, approaching Arizona. "Why don't you put it on?" Brother Arthur asked, gesturing toward the ancient amulet in my hand.

His question startled me, for it was what I'd been thinking.

"Exactly what I had in mind," I said. It had occurred to me that I had always carried the relic in my pocket but had never actually worn it. Perhaps it was merely synchronistic, but I had the uncanny sense that Arthur could read my thoughts.

"I think you'll find it enlightening," he said. I still wore the dark robes of the Russian Orthodox order, and a heavy crucifix hung around my neck, resting on my solar plexus. I lifted the chain over my head and the medallion settled close to my heart, slightly above the cross.

I pondered the events that had torn my life to pieces, remaining convinced that my life would not have been safe even if I'd parted with the jewelled artifact. That evening I had even offered it to Arthur, but he had refused, saying it was not his destiny to become the "bearer of the medallion," as he had put it. He did say, though, that it definitely was his responsibility to see that the fabulous amulet didn't fall into the wrong hands.

Gradually, I fell into a reflective mood, trying to determine what, if any, influence emanated from the talisman. Before long I noticed that my feelings and thoughts seemed more lucid, energized. My disposition lifted, my confidence rose.

Then, unexpectedly, I lost consciousness of my physical surroundings. I became aware of a dim point of light somewhere above me — or perhaps in another dimension of my mind — a light that pulsated softly, changing colors. The light became a luminous mist, and within it appeared a woman, a being of splendor and beauty. Her face was fair, though her features indistinct. From her emanated kindness and warmth like nothing I had ever experienced on earth. My heart rose in expectation and I called out in my mind to the lovely being. She smiled, then began to fade away. But an indescribable sweetness lingered in my heart.

I wasn't able to savor the impression, for another force or being impinged upon my consciousness. It also appeared as a kind of light, yet accompanied not by a sense of loveliness, but of loathing. Slowly the phantom took shape and I beheld a striking countenance — superficially pleasing — yet masking cruelty, menace, and power. It was a human visage, though void of human feeling. It drew closer and I cringed, crying out silently in my mind for the other being of goodness and light. As I did so, the dark spirit of malice drew further away. I could feel a wave of anger flow from it, nearly overwhelming my consciousness. My fingers reached for the medallion and I slipped it over my head. Immediately I became aware of my surroundings — the bus, the sounds of the engine, and Arthur, seated passively at the wheel.

"Well?" asked Arthur, attempting to be casual. His eyes shone with inner brilliance.

"I felt," I said after a long pause, "as if I was at the center of a field of force, a focal point of power." I hesitated.

"Good," said Arthur. "Anything else?"

"I...I...felt the presence of a beautiful being." Arthur glowed when I spoke the words.

"A woman or a man?" Arthur asked.

"A woman," I replied. "Like an angel, a goddess even." Arthur seemed overjoyed.

"But you saw something else, did you not?"

"Yes, there was something else...something horrible, frightening."

Arthur shook his head knowingly.

"Who were they, Brother Arthur?" I asked.

"You must discover that. But I must warn you again. Beware

how you use the medallion. It is a battleground. Opposing forces seek to possess it." Arthur and I fell silent.

I mused on my experience. Could it be that in some inexplicable way I had connected myself with living forces or actual beings in whose hands rested the destiny of the earth?

"Will the medallion protect me in any way?" I said, after many minutes had passed.

"Originally it possessed a protective radiance, yet over the ages numerous influences have become attached to it. Not all of these are beneficial."

"That's not very encouraging."

"If you keep your mood uplifted," said Arthur, "and don't give in to fear or negative states, you should be all right."

"And if I don't?"

Arthur paused a moment. "If you sink into weakness, selfishness or vice, the medallion will accelerate the destruction you bring on yourself." He spoke matter-of-factly, but I shuddered at his words.

"So far, it seems to be destroying me." I stared anxiously at Arthur, hoping he would not confirm my statement.

The old priest yawned, seemingly unaffected by my dilemma. "It's too soon to tell," he said, after a long pause. "As to why you're in this mess, don't blame it on the medallion. You chose this set of circumstances yourself. Certainly you're aware by now that all of us weave the threads of our own destiny."

"It's difficult to believe sometimes. Why would I put myself in this predicament? And the thought of leaving my family, maybe never to see them again. I mean, my daughter...I...I...she means everything to me." My voice trailed off, emotion overpowering me. There was a painful silence before Arthur continued.

"Often the causes of our circumstances lie in the distant past," he said gently. "It's not as if one's contemporary, conscious mind makes all the choices. When we say that we're creators of our own destiny and the masters of our fate, this is most true. Yet we have all lived before...many, many lives. It may be that our Higher Self, or Divine Spirit Presence, selects a particular scenario in a given embodiment so that we may adjust a karmic imbalance and so make progress on our spiritual journey. Growth is hampered until we've removed the obstructions we ourselves have created.

"So many people get bogged down in their lives, seemingly making no progress, just treading water. This happens even to many spiritually-minded people. They end up trapped in their personal, emotional dramas. There is a heaviness about these people, which is literally the case. They're weighed down by unfinished business carried over from the past, often previous incarnations as well as the present. It is visible to a clairvoyant as a dark mass in their aura — psychic baggage in the unconscious.

"Such people often lose their sense of humor and their lightness. Remember that our true nature is light, and this carries a double meaning. We are 'light' in the sense of illumination, and we are 'light' in the sense of lacking heaviness or weight. There will come a time, and it is rather near, when human beings will become almost weightless. They will be so luminous and light-filled that they will actually be able to change density while in the physical body, becoming active in the etheric or subtle dimension that interpenetrates the physical.

"In order to rise to this higher life, there is a key which many people forget. A magic wand by which we transform ourselves from..."

"From frogs to princes, is that the idea?" I said, interrupting Arthur.

"Exactly," replied Arthur, smiling. "This oft-neglected magical power — the wand that transforms us — lies in our will, that is, in our actions.

"For this reason alone we ought always to engage in the doing of good deeds — what in the east is called 'karma yoga.'"

"I can understand that we need to improve our attitudes, becoming positive and so on," I said. "But you're saying that we need to be active serving others in order to rectify past mistakes, and thereby liberate ourselves."

"Exactly. Karma...or the chain of causation that connects an action with its consequences...is not something negative. It is the law of liberation. The goal is the creation of an ideal karma, and this can only be accomplished by living so as to benefit others. In spiritual matters, as well as in material affairs, we can only make true and lasting progress by assisting others through constructive deeds."

"Sounds like course material for a metaphysical Sunday School lesson," I said. "The science and art of doing good."

"Admittedly," remarked Arthur, "performing good works sounds somewhat old-fashioned to the jaded, modern mind. Think of it as engaging in not-so-random acts of kindness. In so doing, one becomes free from past errors and enters a world of true sovereignty. This is liberation. Make no mistake, we must ever be prayerful and engage in daily periods of meditation. But the inner life must be linked with a practical life of service to others...being good and doing good."

"In other words," I said, "we benefit ourselves in proportion to the benefits we give to others. It's another way of expressing the Golden Rule, I suppose."

Arthur nodded in agreement. "According to the divine law of reciprocity, or karma, the circumstances and experiences of our life are the direct results of the causes we ourselves have set in motion by the givingness of our own hands and mind. And if things are less than perfect, look upon them as an opportunity for growth. From the perspective of your Immortal Self, you've created this difficult scenario in order to make amends for past errors and to sow good seeds for the future. It's also a means to strengthen your character and test your development."

"I'm glad my Immortal Self knows what it's doing," I said sarcastically, "but that's small comfort for little old me. I can sympathize with Humpty Dumpty. My whole world is shattered...myself included. How do I begin to pick up all the pieces?"

Arthur smiled and chuckled softly. "All work upon self begins by becoming conscious of your inner life...your life of thought and feeling. Realize that your most inward, private, subjective activity exists not for you alone, but has an effect on the world."

"No man is an island, is that what you're saying?"

Arthur nodded, never taking his eyes off the road. "And nothing occurs in isolation. Our most secret reflections have an influence on others, albeit imponderable. Thoughts and feelings are more real and enduring than objects of the material world."

"I've held that belief my entire adult life...and I've practiced observation of my thoughts for years." I noticed a feeling of pride as I informed Arthur of this.

"Becoming aware of the flow of your consciousness is only the first step. You must become the producer and director...so to speak...of the movies in your mind.

"Think of your thoughts and feelings as a river...a river of consciousness. If the current is muddy, that is, if your inner life is coarse and unrefined, you cannot see to the depths. You must purify your stream of consciousness — the waters of thinking and feeling — by introducing that which is good, beautiful and true. This leads to spiritual vision.

"Take your inner life actively in hand," continued Arthur. "You've seen pictures of charioteers, haven't you?" I nodded. "The impulses and forces of your inner life — your thoughts feelings, desires and so on — are like the horses. You are the charioteer who guides and leads them.

"This brings me to another important truth of life...our inner world creates our outer world. According to the great law of materialization, or manifestation, that which we dwell upon inwardly comes into being in our personal world. When we concentrate upon a pattern of living, we are drawing into our experience the very things we visualize. In other words, our personal environment is the material arrangement...one might say, 'the mirror'...of our mental activity."

"I guess that's why so much emphasis is placed upon concentration and visualization by the metaphysical writers."

"And rightly so. These are the cornerstones of the inner life and the foundation of personal development. Concentration materializes that on which we focus our attention. Visualization is the key to manifestation. What you think about you become."

"So if I control my thinking, I automatically control my environment."

"That's the idea."

In the silence that followed, I reflected on Arthur's words. Although the concepts were not new to me, it was as if I had heard them for the first time. I resolved to take myself in hand more firmly.

"But I still don't have the vaguest idea of what to do with the medallion," I finally blurted out. "I can't sell it. My sense of responsibility won't allow me to pass it off on just anybody. Now I'm running for my life, but don't know where I'm going. Why me?"

Arthur glanced in the rear view mirror before continuing. "If you stay attuned to your inner Presence you'll most certainly be guided. Listen to your intuitive hunches. Learn to read your feelings as you would a book. The universe is constantly revealing to us its secrets, but we don't learn the script. Our life of feelings, if disciplined, is a lantern — a kind of divining rod — by which we may illuminate our way. You yourself are the key that unlocks the mystery of each moment. Remain alert within your cultivated inner listening."

I absorbed Brother Arthur's words, trying to link up to this source of knowledge and illumination within my own mind and heart. After a period of silence, Arthur pulled the van off the road; his words interrupted my revery.

"Let's grab a bite to eat."

"You talked me into it," I said, noticing how hungry I was. If only staying attuned to the divine within one's consciousness was as easy as listening to the promptings of one's stomach, I thought to myself.

"Stick with it and one day it won't be difficult," Arthur said. His words startled me, and again I felt he had deciphered my thoughts.

We sat down at a booth in the plain, "greasy spoon" restaurant beside which we had parked. I stared at the menu, looking in vain for something appealing.

"Biscuits and gravy," I told the middle-aged waitress. "And hold the sausage."

"That'll stick to your ribs," Arthur smiled. He ordered french fries and a grilled cheese on wheat toast. "Not exactly nouveau, California cuisine," he said, "but there's no sauce like hunger."

"It's hard to believe we'll ever become weightless eating this sort of food," I said, taking a sip of the smelly tap water. "I've always noticed there's a connection between the health of my body and the condition of my emotions and my thoughts. What I eat affects my consciousness."

Brother Arthur put his napkin on his lap. "A balanced diet," he said, "composed primarily of grains, vegetables, and fruit is definitely best, and will accelerate one's receptivity to spiritual matters."

"What about meat?" I asked.

"A controversial subject," said Arthur. "Some people may need it. But the meat industry today is not only economically inefficient, it's producing a final product which is loaded with toxins.

"The eating of meat," continued Arthur, "also affects our karma with the animal kingdom...due to the cruelty involved in the whole process. The industrialized slaughter of animals, raised in horrible circumstances, creates a negative condition in humanity which is holding back many people's advancement. Much misery and illness among people today are rooted in the manner in which we treat the animals, who are our little brothers and sisters.

"Diet is certainly important, but keep in mind," he admonished, "that what matters most in terms of truly advancing spiritually is the practice of virtue, that is, the building of character."

"So it's not what I eat, but what eats me," I said. Arthur chuckled.

"And what's eating me right now," I persisted, "besides concern for my family, is anxiety about the powermongers who are out to get the medallion and put an end to me."

"Yes, of course...Ulysses Bundy and his talented cohorts. I admit they represent a formidable and dangerous foe."

"For years I've been reading and hearing about the so-called secret societies," I said, "and the hidden, international government. I couldn't bring myself to believe they actually exist. It now appears I was deceived by my own denial." I lowered my voice as the waitress brought us our food. "How can they be so arrogant as to presume they can rule the world? Just who do these people think they are?"

"Pertinent questions, Jason." Arthur poured a few drops of cream into his coffee before continuing. "But you must first understand that the desire to control the masses is certainly nothing new. It's really as old as the earth.

"Since the dawn of civilization there have been groups of privileged individuals in a dominant position. Nor is this altogether wrong or insidious. It is, in fact, perfectly natural. Those people with the greatest strength, intelligence, energy, ambition, and so forth, will always tend to rise to the top in any society. In fact, throughout almost all of history, most nations have been ruled by an oligarchy, that is, a few individuals with tremendous authority."

I swallowed a mouthful of stale biscuit. "It seems like nowadays it's those with the most money."

"An astute observation," said Arthur. He wiped his mouth and beard on his napkin before continuing.

"In the ancient past, nations and societies were usually ruled by either a priesthood or a monarchy...the Church or the State. These groups generally claimed to have special knowledge or power vested in them by Deity. Oftentimes, they actually did have far greater vision and wisdom than the masses...due in part to the fact that they were groomed for their position from an early age. Also, in the more enlightened cultural epochs, the ruling classes were themselves led or inspired by the centers of learning which I believe are best described by the name Mystery School.

"These were the Temples of Divine Wisdom, and they held sway — at least temporarily — in virtually all ancient cultures that reached a high level of development. These include ancient India, Egypt, China, the Mayan empire of Yucatan, the Incas of Peru, as well as the mother civilizations of Atlantis and Lemuria, or Mu. These latter two continents, which are now beneath the sea...but which shall rise again at the end of this cycle...reached a zenith in spiritual matters toward which our age still strives in vain.

"Although the names of some of these Societies are known to the general culture — the Essenes and Rosicrucians, for example — little is known about the inner workings of these ancient centers of learning. Nonetheless, evidence of the Mystery Schools is to be found everywhere, but perhaps nowhere so obviously as in the ancient pyramids of Egypt and Mexico, and in the megalithic structures such as Stonehenge."

"I've always been fascinated by the idea of Mystery Schools," I commented, "or temples of divine wisdom, in which the deeper truths of life were taught. I believe they existed in the past, but do they have any influence or reality nowadays?"

Brother Arthur leaned slightly forward, as if for greater emphasis. "I assure you from the depths of my heart, Jason: The Schools of heavenly wisdom and initiation have always existed upon the earth and they do so to this day. Of course, their methods differ from epoch to epoch. The true Masters often remain obscure, acting through the agency of their students. These great Masters, or Initiates, are those human beings who have progressed a little farther on the path of spiritual evolution than have the majority."

"How does somebody enter one of these schools?" I asked.

"A candidate enters, not through any external agency, but through an inner contact in the world of spirit."

"But don't they have a physical location as well?"

"Yes," replied Arthur. "But during the last few thousand years these societies have removed themselves from the population centers and are headquartered in remote areas. They seek to influence the various social, political, and religious movements for the welfare of all, but they don't interfere with a person's free will."

"But if the Mystery Schools exist," I protested, "and are trying to inspire the world in a good direction, why is there so much wickedness in high places?"

"The great Teachers and Divine Beings always leave us free to make our own choices, thereby learning from the consequences of our deeds. Unfortunately for humanity, despite the influence of the Mystery Schools and the Initiates, many in leadership positions can't resist the temptation to abuse power for selfish purposes. Even in ancient Atlantis and Egypt a gradual degradation occurred among the ruling class. The priests and pharaohs themselves became corrupted. If people will not be inspired by a moral example, they are easily influenced to enter a dark path.

"So you see," he continued, "we now have a change of format. Those who today have the upper hand in seeking to rule the world are not in the priesthood or the monarchy. They're in the financial power centers, the international banks, multinational corporations, and so forth. Their leadership is in such secretive organizations as the Trilateral Commission, and even more hidden societies. As you said, the ones with the money.

"But keep in mind that the spiritual, political and social institutions of the world, whether they be the Trilateralists, the U.S. Government, the Masons, the established Churches — or even the Boy Scouts for that matter — are essentially a mixture of qualities. Each is a battleground, just as is each human soul. The struggle of Good against Evil, though cosmic in origin and scope, is as intimate and personal as the thoughts, feelings and deeds of each individual."

Brother Arthur's eyes gleamed with an other-worldly passion. His words seared into my soul, and I avoided his gaze. I felt the depth of my own shortcomings, and was ashamed for all the times I had arrogantly passed judgment on the failings of those about me.

"Is it inevitable," I asked, after regaining my composure, "that these elites gain global domination?"

Arthur remained silent as the waitress brought us our bill. He had a far-off look in his eyes. "Sometimes I think it's inevitable that someone — that is, some group — rule the world. If these people were truly enlightened and benevolent, it would probably not be a bad thing. We would then have a society as envisioned by Plato, one of the great initiates of antiquity, who idealized a social system ruled by philosopher-kings...people who had no selfish motive, but, inspired by divine wisdom, sought only to help others.

"But the bottom line is this: What is their motive? As the great Teacher said, 'by their fruits you will know them.' The power elite of today are driving us toward a world of centralized, authoritarian...that is, totalitarian...control, and a resulting loss of individual freedom. Human freedom is sacred.

"In answer to your question...no, it's not inevitable, if enough good people wake up and become spiritually active."

"I read somewhere," I said, "a quote from...Edmund Burke, I believe: 'All that's necessary for evil to triumph is that good men do nothing.'"

Arthur looked at his watch, then sighed. "That about says it all."

We paid for our meal and left the restaurant. My head was buzzing from the conversation, but my stomach felt bloated from the heavy meal. Arthur handed me a bottle of white pills. Take these with you," he said. "You may need them in Mexico."

"Wonder pills?" I asked.

"Anti-toxins. I concocted them myself from various herbs

while travelling in Third World countries for many years." I thanked Arthur and put the bottle in my rucksack.

In the van, an overpowering lethargy got the better of me and I was soon asleep. When I awoke, I was astonished to see the crimson streaks of dawn stretch across the eastern sky.

"We're in Nogales," Arthur said. "Time for you to go."

I was disoriented for several moments, realizing I would no longer have Brother Arthur's companionship. At the same time, I was amazed that he had driven for almost eighteen hours without a rest, on top of delivering the Mass back in Mendocino. Other than some redness in his eyes, he showed no sign of fatigue.

"I suggest you take off your monk's robe," Arthur advised. "It's better you travel as an ordinary person. You still look very different from the man I first met." He pointed to my black glasses and short blonde hair.

I felt vulnerable and alone. "It's all happening so fast," I said. "I feel dazed. Can't you come with me?"

Arthur shook his head. "Don't worry," he said reassuringly. "The divine spirit within you can triumph in even the worst conditions. If you think rightly, miracles will happen."

"But I feel so lost," I said weakly, nearly disconsolate.

"You have a higher power," said Arthur, "always within you and beside you. Invite it to participate. I also have some surprises up my sleeve which must remain a secret for now. You won't be without guidance; this I promise you."

Despite his words of encouragement, I felt mounting anxiety. Arthur sensed my trepidation.

"Don't let fear stand in your way," he said, "To develop courage, one must develop love. Love creates a chalice in the heart capable of holding a divine force. Through love, miracles are made possible. Remember, Jason, it's an honor to be the bearer of the medallion." We fell silent as we drove to the checkpoint for American tourists. The Mexican official waved us through without even bothering to glance at our upheld passports.

"I can't believe it was that easy!" I said.

"That's Nogales for you. It's a big tourist town and they let Americans come through without a hassle. Going the other way is a lot harder." He gestured to the U.S. border.

Arthur pulled the van off the road, stopped, and got out. I grabbed my brown rucksack and went around the van to say goodbye. Arthur met me halfway. He handed me a small, sealed envelope and told me to read the contents when I found myself needing encouragement. We gripped each other's hand.

"Thanks for everything, Arthur. I'm going to miss you." A strange sense of familiarity came over me — almost déjà vu. I felt certain that I had met Arthur somewhere before.

"But we have met before." Arthur's words startled me.

"You were reading my mind!"

"Please excuse me. An annoying habit I've picked up. It's not difficult at all, I assure you. But considering what lurks in most minds, it's hardly worth the effort.

"Yes, Jason, we've met before. At Cornwall, remember? That rainy night along the cliffs with Ricardo?" Brother Arthur reached into his coat pocket and pulled out a flashlight, then handed it to me. I looked at him in absolute astonishment. He smiled warmly, from his heart, and a surge of energy thrilled my frame.

"Never forget," he said, "that the light is infinitely more powerful than the dark. When darkness crowds in around you, become luminous, and walk in the brilliance of your soul."

Arthur turned and strode back to the van. I shook my head in wonder as I watched him pull away, a warm glow filling every cell of my being.

Chapter Ten
A FUGITIVE ABROAD

"Adversity teaches us what nothing else can." E.J.M.

I waited until Arthur's van disappeared from view, then turned and walked down the streets of Nogales. In truth, I barely walked, for it was as if my feet floated on air.

It occurred to me that Arthur could have fabricated the story, based on something Ricardo had told him about our experience in Cornwall. But I dismissed the thought, convinced that Arthur was telling the truth. Surely he was the very man who had so magically come to our aid on the windy cliffs of Tintagel.

Gradually my rapturous mood dissolved, faced as I was with the reality of staying alive in Mexico and reaching my ultimate destination, still unknown to me. As the crimson sun rose above the desert, I sat on a bench in a tiny park to take stock of my situation.

In my rucksack I had minimal possessions: toothbrush, some plastic razors, water purification tablets, a notebook, passport, a few articles of clothing, Arthur's flashlight, and the monk's robe. I had about nine hundred in American money, most of it given to me by George Fort, Ricardo, and Brother Arthur. Deborah had given me a small Spanish phrase book, an English-Spanish dictionary, and a tour guide of Mexico, which included a map.

And of course, there was the medallion.

After stopping at a bank to exchange dollars for pesos, I got on a bus headed toward Guadalajara. I was grateful for the time I'd spent travelling and living in Spain and Peru — about six months in all — and my several vacations in Mexico with Melissa. As a result, I spoke street Spanish and was familiar with the Mexican culture.

My immediate destination was the home of Veronica Fuentes. She and I had been students together, along with Ricardo, fifteen years earlier at Emerson College in southern England.

She came from an upper-crust Mexican family and we'd become close friends. I hadn't seen her, nor kept in touch, since leaving England, but I learned from Ricardo that she had married a wealthy government official. Ricardo had given me her address, the two of them having recently corresponded. Just having a place to go gave me comfort.

The long bus ride was uneventful, although I was mildly irritated by the music — half heavy-metal, half brassy Mexican pop — that the driver constantly had blaring at top volume. No one else seemed to mind; at least there were no complaints. So I attempted to withdraw my consciousness inwardly, seeking inspiration and guidance.

Late that evening I changed buses in Mazatlán, happy to discover a night departure to Guadalajara. The notion of a crowded bus seemed preferable to the lonely isolation of a hotel room. I felt safe and obscure, which was worth the loss of sleep. Besides, I was saving precious pesos.

We reached Guadalajara in the morning and I stepped off the bus near the town center. I ran into an American-style diner to grab a bite to eat. I felt reasonably well considering every-thing, having slept only five or six hours on the bus.

I slid into a booth with a slick table and sticky seats. A heavy-set waiter brought me a glass of water, and I ordered coffee and huevos rancheros. Normally my diet was vegetarian and fairly light. I wondered how my stomach would fare with the heavier Mexican cuisine and notorious Mexican water.

Curiosity got the better of me and I discreetly withdrew the medallion, gazing at the hieroglyphs under the table. I replaced the relic hastily, then pulled out a notebook and pencil from my rucksack. After the experience at Ricardo's house, I was hesitant to dabble with the medallion. But the jewelled treasure exerted an overpowering fascination.

I slowly began tracing one of the glyphs from memory. Immediately, the table began to shake and I stopped abruptly. To my surprise, I noticed that the water in my glass had completely evaporated.

"You are very thirsty, señor," the waiter said to me in Spanish as he stepped up to refill my glass. I bobbed my head, a trifle nervous, and resolved not to try any more tricks in so public a place. It would take months, years even, to fathom the mysterious powers of the Isis Medallion.

Glancing out the window, I noticed an American mini-van with California plates, similar to the one in which Brother Arthur had driven me. In it were two men with clerical collars, apparently Catholic priests. One of them slumped down when I looked through the glass at them. I turned away, stunned by what I'd seen. I was certain the priest who had responded so oddly was none other than Brother Reynard!

I sprang to my feet and scrambled from the booth, rucksack in hand.

"Señor! Your breakfast!" the heavy waiter called out to me as I ran for the door.

"Crazy Gringo!" I heard him say as I rushed into the street. Reeling about, I frantically hailed a taxi. I gave the stocky driver Veronica's address, then fell into the back seat. The taxi lurched into the busy streets of Guadalajara.

My stomach turned and my mind raced, straining to comprehend this startling development. Based on what Brother Arthur had told me about Reynard, it made sense. Rational yet sickening sense.

Brother Reynard had also been a Jesuit prior to joining the Russian Orthodox order. He and Brother Arthur had known each other in Italy, at the Vatican. Arthur had said, half jokingly but obviously in earnest, that he was Reynard's "assignment." He had indicated that, from the Jesuit position, someone with his knowledge could simply not be let loose in the world. I hadn't known what to make of Arthur's assertion. Now I understood. Arthur simply knew too much and had to be watched. Reynard must have been a Jesuit mole whose real duty in the Russian Orthodox chapel was to keep tabs on Arthur. But why had he followed me to Guadalajara? What else did he know?

I clutched the medallion in my pocket, hot flashes pulsing through my body. Might Reynard know of the relic? Had he eavesdropped on our conversations? Or was he privy to a sophisticated, hidden surveillance of which even Arthur was unaware? A horrible thought made me writhe in my seat.

Groping through my rucksack, I pulled out the heavy cross Arthur had given me at the chapel. I examined it carefully, remembering when Brother Reynard had momentarily held it in his hands. My eye fell upon a tiny, metal disc on the underside of the cross. I nearly convulsed, hastily pulling off the disc, which had an adhesive backing. It appeared to be a miniature electronic sensor, possibly a microphone. Alarmed and disgusted, I rolled down the window and threw it into the street. Seconds later, the taxi pulled up in front of the home of Veronica Fuentes.

I paid the driver and ran up the steps towards Veronica's door, aware that we were in one of the wealthiest, most exclusive neighborhoods in Guadalajara. I rang the doorbell, and an attractive, blonde-haired woman, about my age, opened the door. "Veronica!" I said.

"Come in, Jason! Ricardo called me, and I was hoping you would make it." I stepped into Veronica's beautifully decorated home, uncertain whether to hug her or shake her hand. She gave me a warm embrace, and the awkwardness born of a fifteen-year separation instantly dissolved. Veronica led me into an elegant sitting room, and spoke a few words to a young Indian woman dressed in colorful, traditional skirt and blouse. Moments later the young woman brought us orange juice, fresh coffee and biscuits.

"*Muchas gracias,*" I said. "Thanks Veronica, I'm ravenous."

"Help yourself to whatever you'd like," Veronica said, smiling and gesturing towards the kitchen. "Rosita is a wonderful cook. *Mi casa us su casa.*" Veronica spoke flawless American English. Her mother was from Maryland, and she had been educated in an American school in Mexico City.

We looked at each other for a moment, almost shyly.

Veronica was fair-skinned, with a peach complexion and dark brown eyes. When I knew her in England her hair had been straight and long. She now wore it shorter and had it curled. Otherwise, she seemed hardly to have changed at all. She had always been slender. If anything, she now weighed even less.

"I see the years have treated you well, Jason."

"And you, too, Veronica. You're as beautiful as the day I last saw you in England."

Veronica laughed, flashing her cheerleader smile. "Still full of compliments, Jason, you silver-tongued devil. And are you as funny as you used to be?"

"Perhaps to others I am. I think my serious side has gotten the better of the prankster you knew in England. But tell me about you, Veronica. Your home is just beautiful. How is your family?"

Veronica and I caught up on the events of our lives in the interim since we had last seen each other. Her husband, Salvador Fuentes, whom I had never met, had apparently made a small fortune working for Pemex, the nationalized, Mexican oil company. He had recently been appointed to a government position as an aide to one of the national finance ministers in the president's cabinet. His work took him to Mexico City for a good part of the year and he was out of town at that time.

"So Jason, my dear. You must tell me what has brought you to my doorstep. And travelling so lightly." She gestured to my rucksack on the floor. "Ricardo sounded almost anxious when he called, and was rather vague. Are you on a mission for Her Majesty's secret service?"

"In a manner of speaking," I nodded. "Not the Queen of England, mind you. But perhaps the Queen of Heaven."

"Oh, really? You've not become Catholic, have you?"

"Oh no. I'm referring to the goddess in a universal sense. Though surely that would include the Madonna."

"Must we speak in riddles?"

"Veronica, I can't tell you everything at once. I need your help. It's a long story, but someone tried to kill me."

"What! But why, Jason? Your jokes aren't that bad."

"Thanks," I said.

I outlined the events that had brought me to Mexico as a fugitive, without mentioning the relic specifically, referring to it only as an ancient, priceless art piece.

"I'm sorry to drag you into this, Veronica, but I feel desperate."

"Don't apologize. I can use the excitement. The life of an affluent Mexican housewife can be stifling to the spirit."

"I'm afraid the danger far exceeds the excitement. Someone even followed me to your house. I honestly don't know what to do next."

"Listen, I have an idea," she said, tossing her blonde hair.

"I'm all ears."

"I was planning to meet my husband tomorrow in Mexico City. He is attending a rather secretive financial meeting with his boss, Orlando Santini. I wanted to visit the shrine of Our Lady, the Virgin of Guadalupe."

"Oh really. A pilgrimage?" I asked. Veronica smiled.

"Visiting sacred sites is good for the soul," she said.

"So you've developed a connection to the Blessed Mother, too."

Veronica winked. "In a universal sense. You know that 'Sophia' means wisdom. Perhaps the Madonna is the Divine Sophia of today, a modern representation of the ancient and eternal mother goddess of humanity, the perfect blend of love and wisdom."

"You're probably right," I said, inwardly quickened as our dialogue touched on one of my favorite topics.

"At any rate," Veronica continued, "why don't you come with me? Salvador won't mind. He's really very modern and broad-minded. He will be happy for me to reconnect with an old friend. We'll be staying at an exclusive hotel, and I can see to it that you get a room. Don't worry about the cost; I'll see to everything."

"That sounds wonderful!" I said, my spirits uplifted. "At

least it's a next step...I'm making this up as I go." I paused for a moment. "What kind of meeting did you say Salvador is attending?" I asked, not quite sure if it were my business.

"Oh, it's one of those elite, private meetings of the international financiers...where they don't allow the press to get near. The Trilateral Commission, I think he said."

"The Trilateral Commission!" I exclaimed, unable to conceal my astonishment.

"Why, yes. You know about them, do you? But of course you would, Jason. You were always into everything obscure and mysterious. I remember us talking about secret societies back in England. Although I recall you were rather skeptical of conspiracy theories at the time."

"I've had cause to reconsider," I said, placing my elegant china cup back on its saucer. Veronica paused to refill it with coffee before continuing.

"Salvador's boss, Orlando Santini, is a member of the Trilateral Commission. Mexico, in case you haven't already gathered the fact, is almost entirely controlled by an elite ruling class. As destiny would have it, I've married into the modern aristocracy."

"Absolutely amazing!" I said, my mind filled with wonder at the unseen, guiding hand that seemed to direct my steps.

The phone rang as we were conversing and I overheard Rosita answer it in the hallway. I made out the words, "*Si, está aqui, está aqui.*"

I sprang to my feet, crying out to Veronica, "Don't let anyone know I'm here!" She raced to the phone and took it from Rosita.

"Hello, who is it?" she asked. By that time I was standing beside her and could hear the click on the other end. Rosita told us the caller had been a man wanting to know if a young American gentleman had arrived at Veronica's home. Having not been instructed to say otherwise, she had innocently said "Yes."

"Damn!" I muttered. "They know I'm here. I wish we were

leaving today."

"Don't worry, Jason," Veronica cooed, trying to soothe my anxiety. "Who knows? It may even have been Ricardo or one of your friends, just wanting to let Melissa know that you were safe."

"Maybe," I said doubtfully, staring at the telephone. "Let's hope so."

I tried to forget the phone call as Veronica and I extended our conversation through the afternoon, until dinner, at which time I met her charming, ten-year-old son, Miguel. It occurred to me that this sweet-faced, innocent boy, by virtue of his birth in a well-placed Mexican family, might one day be groomed for a position of leadership in the international ruling class. I remembered Arthur's words that by no means were all of the elites bad; some indeed were very advanced souls. Good and evil were not clearly delineated and separate, as in a fairy tale. Real life was a battleground between these polarities, and the battlefield was the human soul itself.

I retired early that evening. Veronica showed me to an elegant guest room with a private bath and jacuzzi. "We had this put in especially for the occasional visit of Orlando Santini, or one of the elite bureaucrats with whom Salvador now rubs shoulders. It's a different world, Jason. Did you think this morning that you would be sleeping in a bed meant for a Trilateralist?"

"The irony's unbearable. I didn't know if I'd even be sleeping in a bed tonight. I can't thank you enough for your hospitality, Veronica."

"Don't think twice about it, my dear. The pleasure of your company is more than enough recompense." Veronica winked and said goodnight. I collapsed upon the bed, exhausted, intending to reflect on the day's surprising events before showering. Within seconds I fell into a deep and dreamless sleep.

Chapter Eleven
MEXICO CITY

"Wisdom is to the soul what milk is to a babe." E.J.M.

The next morning I awoke early, fully dressed. I indulged for fifteen minutes in the hot, swirling waters of the jacuzzi, my thoughts wandering over the astonishing events of the previous days.

I assumed Brother Reynard knew of the medallion. There was no other reason for him to have followed me. I supposed that he also must have learned of it as a Jesuit, or while at the Vatican, much the same as Arthur. And it seemed reasonable that the Jesuits would do their utmost to regain the relic, which centuries before had been in their hands. After all, the Roman Catholic Church was certainly no stranger to fantastic wealth and awesome global power. Might not the inner circle of the Church hierarchy covet the medallion in order to assist them in their worldly ambitions for dominance — temporal as well as spiritual?

I showered and went downstairs. Veronica had stepped out, leaving me a note with breakfast, which was served to me by Rosita, the friendly Indian woman in the colorful attire. The note said we would leave before nine o'clock. After eating, I occupied myself by writing in my notebook — experimenting with a coded language only I could understand — and attempting carefully to incorporate the inscrutable medallion hieroglyphs.

Most of the symbols were completely alien to me. But I did recognize the famous Egyptian cross — the ankh, or *crux ansata* — which appeared several places on both sides of the relic. I knew that the ankh — composed of a circle above a cross — was symbolic of the Spirit's control of matter, and that it represented eternal life. I sensed that the deeper mysteries of the medallion, to which Arthur had referred, were somehow connected to the significance of the ankh.

My eye fell upon the geometric floral design at the center

of the sun. The Flower of Life, Arthur had called it. I had remarked to him that it did not appear particularly Egyptian. He had replied that it was one of the most ancient symbols, pre-dating the Egyptian civilization, but that it could be found as part of a larger flower pattern on a temple wall in Abydos. The temple was in honor of Osiris, husband of Isis, and dedicated to the resurrection — again a cryptic reference to life eternal.

Veronica returned at eight, having driven Miguel to his school. She playfully peeked over my shoulder as I dabbled in my notebook. "Playing connect-the-dots, are you, Jason? Small minds are easily amused." I smiled at her teasing.

"Actually, I'm writing down everything intelligent that I've ever heard you say. It's been an hour now and the pages are still blank." Veronica laughed and disappeared into her room.

Minutes later, she appeared by the door holding a couple of sleek travel bags. She looked stunning in her rose-colored outfit. "You look ready to take on the world," I said.

"You mean, I don't look like a humble pilgrim visiting the Shrine of Our Lady?" Veronica asked facetiously, displaying her dazzling smile.

"You never were traditional; perhaps you'll start a trend."

I donned one of Salvador's dashing sport coats, then selected a pair of mirrored sunglasses from a bureau drawer. We carried our bags outside and down the steps, where a white limousine was waiting. Veronica smiled at the driver, speaking to him in Spanish. Minutes later, we were on the road east to Mexico City.

"What's the matter?" Veronica asked, noticing my unease.

"I can't help thinking we're being followed," I answered, looking at the traffic behind us.

"Based on everything you told me yesterday, Jason, I'd be rather surprised if we were not. But don't worry too much. I've taken precautions."

"Precautions?" I said, raising my eyebrows. Veronica pointed to a blue BMW following not far behind us.

"See those two men in the blue car? That's Ernesto and Oscar. They're on our side. One might call them bodyguards. Because Salvador is so often out of town, he's made sure I have someone to call upon if I need. So please don't make any indiscreet advances." Veronica winked.

"Are you flirting with me again, Veronica?" I asked teasingly.

"Who, me? We've had our fling, haven't we, Jason?"

"Yes," I nodded, "that chapter is closed." We fell into a brooding silence. Veronica and I had formed a close bond at Emerson College, part of a group in which numerous tight friendships were formed. We had one brief, passionate weekend, almost destroying the beauty of our previously platonic rapport. After weeks of avoiding each other, we had reconciled, both of us recognizing that the nature of our special friendship was not meant to be physical.

I waved my hand at a pestering insect. "Time's sure fun when you're having flies," I said, breaking the silence. "I have to admit I have the horrible feeling I'm moving right into the jaws of a trap."

"A very dramatic scenario, to be sure," said Veronica. "Reminiscent of a Shakespeare play."

"Let's hope it doesn't turn out to be a tragedy."

"It's not like you to be a pessimist, Jason. What is it you always used to say? Positive energy is stronger than gravity."

"Yes, I still believe that's true. I guess we all need to be reminded. Tell me what you know about the Trilateralists."

"Not much more than you, probably. Salvador really confides very little to me about that aspect of his work. He isn't much more than an assistant...a glorified secretary, not one of the power-brokers himself. We're just along for the ride.

"But I suppose," she continued, "they represent the modern patriarchal mechanism of control. It seems all they're concerned about is bombs and money. The whole planet is being destroyed by the greed of these corporate wizards and global financiers. Why can't they understand that the earth is sacred?"

"I wish I knew, Veronica." I told her about a seminar George and I had once attended on saving the rainforest and the global environment. The conference was full of idealistic young people — mostly college students — who were motivated by the best of intentions. George and I had discovered, to our dismay, that the conference had been devised, sponsored, and paid for by a consortium of major international banks and multi-national corporations. They had tried to sell the conferees on the wisdom of putting the South American rainforest into trust to protect it from commercial exploitation. What they didn't say was that they — that is, the elite financiers and corporate magnates who were pushing the idea — would themselves own and "manage" the trust, thus enabling them to do as they pleased with the rainforests, under the false cover of environmentalism.

"Perhaps," I continued, "we can learn from the old traditions that revered the Great Mother and perceived that God also had a feminine face."

"Yes, the Sophia tradition," said Veronica, "the emanation of heavenly wisdom in myriad forms. Not only have women been marginalized by the dominant culture of recent centuries, but the Divine Feminine has been suppressed."

"Suppressed, but not extinguished," I said. "Perhaps the Holy Spirit, third aspect of the Christian Trinity, is actually the ancient Sophia, the divine feminine. It represents intuition and imagination — the whole feeling dimension. And then there's Mother Mary, arguably the most popular representation of the spiritual feminine at any time in world history."

"Maybe you're right," Veronica acknowledged. "But Sophia needs to re-emerge in a more conscious and obvious manner. And the wisdom tradition that she nurtures has to replace rigid orthodoxy and blind belief. Of all the ancient expressions of Woman as Divinity, my favorite is Isis."

"Oh really?" I said. "Why is that?"

"She was so exalted, so loving and compassionate by nature — so full of wisdom and devotion. She was also powerful, a Creator. Without her influence, earthly culture would have remained in a primitive condition. According to the Isis and Osiris myth, the evil Set — Egyptian equivalent of the Christian Satan — succeeded in cutting up into many fragments Isis' husband, the divine Osiris. It was the great work of Isis to discover and restore to wholeness her Beloved's body, thus restoring him to life."

I was silent a moment, pondering the deeper meaning of the myth. "Perhaps," I said, "that is the task of the divine feminine today. That is, to re-assemble the scattered wisdom of the ancient world, bringing God — in the fullest sense — back to life."

"Yes," Veronica agreed, "and to resurrect the human race at the same time."

We fell quiet, enjoying the rugged scenery along the way, and by late afternoon were on the outskirts of Mexico City. We made our way through the enormous and terribly overcrowded metropolis toward the posh luxury hotel where the Trilateralists were to meet.

The limousine stopped in front of the hotel lobby and Veronica and I got out. "*Muchas Gracias,* Diego," she said to the chauffeur.

"I'll take our bags," I said, draping the straps over my shoulders. We walked into the ornate lobby to the reservation counter. Veronica had already reserved a room for me, and we had only to get our keys.

I stood behind a tall, imposing man in a blue business suit. Probably a C.E.O., I said to myself. The man picked up his briefcase, then turned abruptly to look at something. I stared straight into the piercing eyes of Ulysses Bundy!

Chapter Twelve
THE PILGRIM AND THE PRISONER

"We are each the star of our life's drama — possibly because no one else wanted the part." E.J.M.

I squeezed Veronica's arm, then vanished into the bathroom. Never could I have imagined being so eternally grateful for the invention of mirrored sunglasses.

After regaining my composure, I returned to the lobby and hovered off to one side, seeking the shelter of a large pillar. Veronica picked up our keys and appeared beside me. "You obviously didn't like that man's face," she whispered. "Or was it his outfit?"

"This is no time for jokes, sweetheart. That was Ulysses Bundy. The man I told you about."

"I'll make a point not to introduce the two of you," Veronica said. "Let's see what the rooms are like, shall we?" We took the elevator to the ninth floor, and walked down the plush carpet to our suites. My room — adjoining that of Veronica and Salvador — was number 913.

"Damn!" I muttered under my breath.

"What's the matter?" asked Veronica. "Too shabby for you?"

"It's the number. I don't like thirteen."

"Oh come on, you're not superstitious, are you?"

"No. It's just that numbers have qualities. Thirteen for me has always meant decisive, powerful change."

"That's not necessarily bad," comforted Veronica. "According to the ancient Mayan system, thirteen means the end of a cycle and the beginning of a new one."

"I just don't know," I said, shrugging my shoulders, "if I can take any more sudden changes. I guess I'll just have to accept the fact that transformation is what this is all about." Veronica went down to the lobby to await her husband's arrival, while I sequestered myself in my room, feeling more and more like a hostage.

I didn't yet regret the decision to come with Veronica to

Mexico City. But my consternation was growing. It was likely that Brother Reynard, or some of his cronies, had followed us to the hotel. They could easily have bugged Veronica's limousine with one of those electronic sensors. And the hotel was crawling with the Trilateralist crowd. The amazing thing was that I had come willingly!

My hand reached into my jacket pocket, as if pulled there by a force outside myself, and clutched the silver box containing the medallion. I reflexively pulled it out and carefully opened the clasp. I stared at the beautiful amulet, my eye tracing the obscure symbols.

A curious feeling came over me. Perhaps now, I thought to myself, in this hotbed of the global powermongers, I could seek to ally myself with the medallion's power. Impulsively, I put the chain around my neck and closed my eyes.

I was in the habit of visualizing a protective light when calling upon the divine world, but a strange and melodious voice, soothing and seductive, distracted me. The voice advised me to relax, to let go and enjoy the pleasures of life.

"Stop running and hiding," the voice implored. Great riches and power could easily be mine. "Seek out the help of those wiser than you," it suggested. Go and give the medallion to the good and responsible people who sought it. They would take care of it, and I would be richly rewarded for my efforts.

Abruptly, the voice became an image, clear and distinct, and a being of power and intelligence appeared before me — a spectre from the world of shadows. I recognized the forbidding presence I had briefly encountered while wearing the medallion in Arthur's van. The phantom's eyes, cold as steel, cut through my soul. I shivered and my blood crawled. I sensed that behind a stark veneer of beauty, there breathed a hideous, chilling, and utterly ruthless strength. Nor did it radiate, but rather I felt pulled into the vortex of the being's power, entranced.

My limbs grew heavy and cold. I felt immobilized, frozen. I knew that if I did not soon get up, I would be consumed by the diabolic apparition. I shuddered violently, and with enormous difficulty clasped the medallion still hanging around my neck. Breaking my paralysis, I stood up and heaved the pendant far away.

Instantly I regained awareness of my physical where-abouts. I still sat in my chair. The medallion lay harmlessly in my hand; I had only imagined hurling the relic. My heart was pounding, and I had broken out in a cold sweat. I crammed the medallion into its case and stuffed it inside my jacket.

My ragged nerves were jolted by the ringing of the tele-phone. I jumped nervously from the chair, determined not to answer it. It chimed a dozen times before finally stopping. After a minute or so, the phone rang again. This continued for almost an hour: twelve rings followed by a minute's silence, then the phone again. Finally, I could stand it no longer. Quivering, I picked up the phone.

"Hello," I whispered. There was a brief silence on the other end. Then a click. I felt like an animal in a trap.

There was a coffee maker on the bureau and I brewed a pot. "At least I can die in a luxurious setting," I thought to myself. The grisly thought made me shiver and I countered it with more hopeful affirmations.

I reached for some sweet Mexican cookies I had brought with me from Veronica's kitchen, and began dipping them in the coffee. A tap on the door made me bolt to my feet.

"It's me, Veronica," came the voice.

"Come in," I said softly, going back to my snack. Veronica came in and closed the door behind her. I was relieved to have her company.

"What!" she exclaimed in mock surprise. "You dip your cookies in your coffee! You big wimp!"

"Oh, leave me alone," I said. "I feel like an inmate on death row. You don't know of anyone who might be trying to call this suite?" I asked, then explained the odd series of phone calls.

Veronica shook her head. "The suite is registered in my and Salvador's name. I have no idea."

I made an effort to compose myself, trying mentally to downplay the phone calls and to forget my frightening encounter with the spectre.

"Cheer up," Veronica said with a smile. "You don't want to live forever, do you?" Her attempt at humor failed miserably. "I want you to meet my husband," she continued. Veronica opened the door and in stepped a handsome, black-haired man with a trim moustache and refined features. I stood up and shook hands with Salvador. His gracious smile put me at ease, and I liked him instantly.

"It's a pleasure to make your acquaintance," he said. "Veronica has told me so much about her Emerson College days. Now I have living proof she wasn't making it all up." Salvador's English was fluent.

"At least not all of it," I said, grinning.

"Other than to see old friends, what brings you to Mexico?"

"I needed a break from my work," I explained. "You know how it is — stress and all that. I hope to make it to Yucatan, to the pyramids."

"They are fascinating," said Salvador. "What line of work are you in?"

"I'm sort of a communication's liaison, travelling between corporations and law firms in San Francisco," I said, slightly embarrassed at my modest occupation.

"Oh yes," said Salvador, "we have them here in Mexico City as well. We call them couriers. Can I get you a drink, or something from room service?"

"Thank you, but I'm fine," I responded, feeling very humble.

"Jason has travelled through much of the world, and has taught elementary school and junior high," said Veronica. "He's an original thinker...a student of life. And he's currently making a study of the international, financial power elite." Veronica winked at me.

"Oh really," said Salvador. "So you've come here to spy on us?"

"Oh no, nothing like that," I said defensively. "It's pure

coincidence."

"I wasn't serious," said Salvador reassuringly. "But you know about the Trilateral Commission, do you?"

"A little bit," I said.

"Don't feel you need to hide anything, Jason." Veronica said. "Salvador's not really one of them. Are you, my dear?" Veronica smiled teasingly.

"Certainly not in spirit," he said. "Politically and spiritually I am more aligned with your Thomas Jefferson. Now, there was a true statesman and philosopher. If he knew what some of your countrymen and the others here at this meeting were planning, he would most certainly roll in his grave."

"Can you give us a hint?" Veronica asked.

Salvador loosened his tie and sat in one of the luxurious chairs. "This is basically a regional — that is, North American — conference," he began, "sponsored by Banco Mexicano, along with some major U.S. Banks."

"That explains Ulysses Bundy," said Veronica.

"You know Dr. Bundy?" Salvador asked me.

"I know *of* him," I said discreetly.

"At any rate, you see, they wish to create the legislative architecture of a new international system. A kind of first step to a global network of financial and political control. They'll call it 'free trade,' but it's really about absolute government control of free enterprise.

"The long-term goal, of course, is to integrate all regional governments — European, North American, and so on — into increasingly larger government cartels. These would ultimately merge to form a centralized, global super-state."

"Hello Big Brother, goodbye individual liberty!" said Veronica.

"The Trilateralist plan," Salvador explained, "along with those of its various domestic counterparts — such as the CFR in your country — is to create this New World Order, with the financial elites at the helm, and institute taxes and controls on an international level, as well as federal, state, and community level. And there would, of course, have to be a global, inter-national military, and a worldwide police force."

"Can you imagine!" Veronica fumed. "Paying income tax to a totalitarian world government, in addition to federal, state and local taxes. And for what? So Big Brother can have a global gestapo to control us poor sheep!" I thought back to the con-versations I had shared with George, feeling fresh admiration for his viewpoints.

"They also want to eliminate cash," Salvador persisted, "and go exclusively to credit cards, which should more accu-rately be called 'debit cards.' This would create a kind of debt slavery, and all transactions could be traced and taxed. The underground economy would be eliminated, raising additional, huge tax revenues for the elites."

"Ingenious," said Veronica, shaking her head.

"And terrifying," I added. I thought back to my courier days in San Francisco, and the time I had accidentally entered the inner chambers of the Federal Reserve Bank. Many of the papers and writings which I had seen were about the Fed's intention to eliminate cash. It dawned on me that they must have considered this a prerequisite to complete economic and political control.

"Yes," said Salvador. "I've always admired the freedoms you Americans have inherited from your wise forefathers. But soon, if all goes as these financiers and plutocrats intend, you'll be as impoverished and subdued as most Mexicans."

I was intrigued that Salvador would be so forthcoming in his revelation of the financial elite's true motives. I hoped he would elaborate further. "So all this I've read over the years," I continued, "about a hidden, international clique seeking global control isn't just the paranoid ravings of society's discontents, but is actually rooted in fact."

Salvador gave a thin smile. "It certainly stretches one's credulity to the utmost. But as an employee of the elites, and something of an insider myself, I assure you that these are not just wild conspiracy theories. They are facts.

"Through control of a nation's economy, the power elites influence and manipulate government. And they employ a compliant media, which they largely own, as their instrument of mind control."

"The manufacture of consent," I said.

Salvador nodded, then continued. "And from what I can tell, the leadership of the elites — groups such as the Trilateral Commission and others even more secretive — have an unholy alliance, not only with government...which is composed mostly of their lackeys...but also with the criminal underworld of the Mafia, the drug cartels, and so on.

"They're by no means all bad people...the drug hoodlums notwithstanding. Some very idealistic souls get attracted by the globalist rhetoric. I myself was once convinced that their aims were good. But I now believe those in the inner circle don't have the best interests of humanity at heart. They seek their own selfish gain.

"The reason paranoia springs up in so many people's minds is that you have a group of incredibly wealthy and powerful people attempting to keep their aims and purposes secret, not to mention their very existence. People fear the unknown. And I assure you, people certainly have reason to be concerned about the intentions of these elites."

"A bleak scenario, but I don't think they'll succeed," I said, feeling unexpectedly confident. I was surprised by my own statement.

"Any particular reason?" Salvador asked.

"Just a hunch," I replied, shrugging my shoulders.

"I'm not particularly religious," said Salvador, "at least not in a traditional sense. But to stop them it may take no less than divine intervention." Our conversation was interrupted by the telephone ringing, which Veronica answered.

"It's for you, Salvador," she said, handing the phone to her husband. "It's Orlando Santini." Salvador took the phone and spoke quietly to his boss. He grew disturbed by the conversation, turning pale.

"I understand, sir," he said. "I understand." Salvador stared at me piercingly. "I'll do what I can. He just left the room on his way up to the roof...to take in a view of the city, I believe." He raised his eyes in alarm and I started to my feet. "Don't worry. I'm sure he won't get away." He slammed down the phone, unable to hide the anxiety in his eyes.

"They're after you, my friend." he said. "I had no idea you were such a VIP. You must run now!"

"Come with me!" Veronica insisted, taking my arm.

"But where?" I asked, trembling with fear.

"To the Shrine of Our Lady!" she whispered, heading for the door. "You know...divine intervention!"

I threw the Russian Orthodox gown over my head, the dry taste of terror in my mouth. Only a miracle could save me now. We ran out the door to the elevator, taking us to the lion's den below.

Chapter Thirteen

OUR LADY OF GUADALUPE

"Death is not dying, but a birth,
Which binds together heaven and earth." E.J.M.

The elevator opened onto the crowded lobby and we raced toward the front door — nearly knocking over a bellboy on the way. "Stop them!" a loud voice cried.

I turned my head and saw some men in black suits start toward us. They looked like the secret-service types I had seen at the chapel in Mendocino.

Veronica and I bolted through the front door, relieved to see our white limo pull up at that moment, with Diego at the wheel. Salvador must have called the chauffeur on his cellular phone.

"Don't let them get away!" came a shout from behind, as Trilateral agents streamed out of the lobby.

The blue BMW with Veronica's bodyguards raced up behind our limo. Fernando and Oscar got out, with pistols drawn, as Diego pressed the accelerator. "To the Basilica of Our Lady!" shouted Veronica.

To my horror, shots rang out, followed instantly by the cry of stricken voices. I turned in time to see Fernando and Oscar collapse to the ground.

"Oh my God!" I gasped. Veronica and I instinctively hunched down in the back seat as Diego whisked us away. My skin crawled with fright and it was all I could do to keep my composure. The realization of my predicament weighed on me like an executioner's block.

Fortunately, the Basilica was near the hotel and it seemed mere seconds before we were there. *"Vaya con Dios!"* Diego shouted as we sprinted up the steps of the old church. There were dozens of pilgrims outside the cathedral, some of them kneeling in reverence and prayer. Several priests reached the massive doors seconds before us, attempting to block our path.

"That robe never did quite fit you," one of them said, a cold sneer on his face. It was Brother Reynard.

"Life is full of masquerade and pretense, isn't that what you told me?" I said, shoving him out of the way. I was surprised that my contempt for Reynard overshadowed my terror. Veronica slapped another priest who tried to delay her.

"That's no way to behave toward a lady," she scowled. We darted through the doors into the sacred atmosphere of the holiest shrine in Mexico.

"We made it this far; now what?" I asked, shivering. We paused to catch our breath. There were hundreds of pilgrims and worshippers in the quiet, crowded cathedral. Brother Reynard and his fellow Jesuits were coming in the door. Behind them entered the forbidding men in black suits.

"This way," Veronica whispered, clasping my arm. We ran down the central aisle toward the altar. On the wall behind the podium was a large and beautiful statue of the Madonna, appearing as the Virgin of Guadalupe. An overwhelming inner force — a beneficent compulsion — made me fall to my knees. My fear vanished, replaced by awe. Instantly, I began to pray — to God, to the Blessed Mother, and the holiest of angels. My silent petition poured forth from the depths of my heart.

"Arrest him!" barked a harsh voice from behind me. "Everyone out of the way." Pilgrims began to whisper, then a loud murmur arose from the astonished onlookers.

"Not in the holy sanctuary," came another voice. I recognized the shrill tones of Brother Reynard. "He is under the protection of the Holy Church, and we shall take custody of him."

"Leave him alone!" came a third voice, resounding with authority and filling me with amazement. "I believe I have what you seek." Serenely I rose to my feet and turned around, astounded by the voice.

It was Brother Arthur, arrayed in a dazzling white garment, trimmed in purple and gold. A large silver cross hung at his chest, and in his upraised hand he held a shimmering, golden medallion. The Medallion of Isis!

Several of the secret-service types drew handguns from their coats. "You may take his soul," one of them cried out. "But leave his body to us!" A shot exploded, and Arthur clutched his heart, mortally stricken. Instantly, screams and terrified shouts filled the crowded cathedral.

"Arthur!" I shouted, stepping toward him. His gaze fell upon me, a supernatural light illumining his countenance. A look of divine majesty touched his features. He smiled at me, a radiance shining from his eyes. It was the look of a soul gazing upon the glories of Paradise. Brother Arthur slumped, dying, to the floor.

As pilgrims streamed chaotically toward the door, several brave and noble souls carried Arthur to the front of the Basilica. They laid him gently at the feet of the Virgin of Guadalupe; roses on the altar showered him with petals. The Medallion of

Isis remained in his right hand, held in the grip of death. Many weeks later I learned that it was only with the aid of tools that they were able to pry the relic free.

In the frenzy, Veronica and I ran with other pilgrims toward the door. We stepped out of the Basilica into the declining rays of evening. I seemed to be in trance, yet rarely had I felt so conscious and serene.

Salvador met us on the steps, grabbing each of us by the arm. "Come with me," he said urgently. We charged down the steps of the Basilica and into the white limousine. Diego raced off, and in what seemed but a flicker, we were at the rear of the luxury hotel.

Speeding from the limo, we headed up a freight elevator to the hotel roof. There at the top, waiting for us, was a black, unmarked helicopter.

"Courtesy of Orlando Santini!" shouted Salvador, above the roar of the chopper. "It will get you to the countryside. From there you're on your own. I wish you God-speed!" He hurriedly shook my hand, then embraced Veronica. They exchanged some words I could not hear, then she and I climbed into the aircraft. Seconds later we were in the air, flying rapidly over the darkening city skyline.

Almost as a reflex I reached into my pocket. There in its silver case was the medallion. I turned and gazed, wonderingly, at the Basilica of the Virgin of Guadalupe, watching until it became an indiscernible speck in the Mexico City twilight.

BOOK TWO
A Glimpse of Paradise

"The divine Sophia have I loved and sought from my youth; I have desired her to be my spouse. Ever have I loved her beauteous, radiant form. Ever have I prayed that she might be sent to abide with me, that she might work with me to the end that I might know what I lacked and what in me God would find acceptable. And since she had ever known and understood, had guided me in all my life's activity, I am persuaded that even after death she will ever keep me safe, wrapped securely in her watchful, constant love."
—Giordano Bruno

Chapter One
YUCATAN

"Wisdom has two parents: Joy and Sorrow." E.J.M.

Veronica and I were silent, gathering our thoughts. It was clear to me that Brother Arthur had employed a false medallion, a clever fake. It would not take long for our predators to discover this, but Arthur's supreme sacrifice had enabled us to escape. We had prayed for a miracle and it had materialized; the cost was more than I could bear to contemplate.

We were in the air several minutes before I realized I was trembling. My whole mind and body were stunned — disbelieving — and my heart was overcome with gratitude to Arthur. I was too shocked to weep.

"That was Brother Arthur, wasn't it?" Veronica asked, breaking a long silence. I nodded, speechless. "What he had in his hand...is that truly what they were after?" I shook my head, then reached into my pocket and pulled out the medallion.

"It was a fake. This is the real one." I took the shining relic from its container and held it up to Veronica's gaze. She examined it carefully, almost reverently, then sighed and looked away. "One day, I'll tell you why they desire it so badly. As you can guess, it's not just because of its material value."

I stared at Veronica. Her expression was forlorn and distant. "Is it Fernando and Oscar? I asked.

She shook her head. "It's everything. I hardly knew the two of them, but it seems so needless and tragic."

"Yes, I know."

"You know, Jason, I have to confess I only half-believed what you were telling me about being chased, and everything. I should have been far more cautious. I'm sorry."

"Don't bother about it."

There was another long silence. Veronica bit her lip. "But there's more," she said. "I feel so guilty and stupid."

"Why's that?"

"The first time Ricardo called, before you arrived, he was very cautious, very discreet. But I was flippant and careless, treating his caution as a joke. It wouldn't surprise me if our phone was tapped. I probably tipped them off."

"Don't worry about it, Veronica. Without you I'd have been lost in the first place. I know it seems crazy, but somehow I feel everything will work out. Arthur gave his life. Such a sacrifice can't be in vain."

After another long pause I asked, "Where are we going — do you know?"

"Not far in the chopper. Just a short ways out of Mexico City. Salvador has put himself at considerable risk. Because Orlando Santini trusts him so much, Salvador has clearance to get one of these helicopters in emergency situations. Needless to say, this isn't the kind of emergency he had in mind. The pilot doesn't know who we are. Let's just hope no one calls him on the radio and orders him back."

Fortunately, the craft was in the air less than half an hour. We touched down in an empty field, jumped to the ground, and watched as the helicopter flew off.

We walked about a mile to a small tienda frequented by Indians. Veronica spoke to several men standing outside. One of them hurried off and in minutes drove up in a beat-up, old Ford truck. We climbed in the back and rode in silence for two hours. The driver pulled off the narrow, asphalt road onto a rough dirt lane, and soon we reached a dilapidated peasant shanty of the type so numerous throughout the impoverished country, and in which the majority of Mexicans made their home.

"This is the home of Rosita's family," Veronica said. "The servant lady whom you met at my home. They're of Mayan descent and completely trustworthy. They'll help you reach Yucatan safely."

We knocked on the door of the small house; Veronica spoke to an elderly woman for several minutes in Spanish. At one point she reached into her purse and pressed a thick wad of pesos into the woman's hand. The dark-haired grandmother thanked Veronica profusely.

"Jason, I hate to leave you now, but I must get back to my family. Salvador and Miguel need me, and I would only draw attention to you anyway. These are good people. They will help you."

"Veronica, I can never thank you enough."

"You know there's no need to, Jason. I only wish I could help you more. Take care. My prayers are with you."

"I'll be all right," I said. "I don't understand it, but I know I'll find what I'm looking for in Yucatan. And I'll come and see you again soon; you just watch." I forced myself to smile.

"I hope so, dear friend." Veronica took my hands in hers. "This time, don't wait fifteen years to get in touch."

"I promise. And I won't be a fugitive, either."

We embraced in the dim light of the kerosene lanterns, then she kissed my cheek and walked back to the truck. I watched, desolate, as she disappeared into the blackness of the night.

When I awoke at sunrise, the entire Indian family was awake, gazing at me curiously. The grandmother smiled and handed me some clothes. I understood they would be my new wardrobe.

I changed behind the house, trying to be modest, as several dogs sniffed at my feet and three young children stood nearby, giggling. My new attire was typical Indian dress: a brightly colored woven shirt, plain black trousers — which I rolled up above the ankle — and a pair of Mexican sandals, replete with rubber-tire soles. I still had my passport, money, and a few personals in my backpack, which Salvador had the presence of mind to toss from the limo into the helicopter.

I gave my American clothes to Rosita's brother, Santos, who would be my guide. He smiled broadly, revealing brilliant, white teeth. I kept the black priest's robe — perhaps because of Arthur. After a breakfast of beans and tortillas, washed down with instant Nescafe, we hit the road.

Santos' car was a depressingly beat-up old Toyota. Veronica had bought it, secondhand, for Rosita ten years earlier. Somehow Santos kept it running.

Santos was cheerful, yet quiet. He could see I was not in the mood to talk. He told me, when I asked, that we were slightly west of the town of Orizaba — that it would be a two-day trip to Yucatan.

The day was uneventful, which was fine by me. My mind and my body were numb. It was difficult to focus my thoughts and I seemed unable to reflect on events. Arthur had given me several meditations which I employed ceaselessly. One was to visualize a golden star, shining radiantly above me — an emblem of my Higher Self. Another was to picture a delicate, pink rose — symbol of loving-kindness — in the region of my etheric heart. I asked constantly for guidance, and protection for myself and my loved ones. I could not bring myself to think of Arthur except to cherish a profound gratitude, akin to reverence, for the greatness of the man and his awesome sacrifice.

After nightfall, we pulled off the main road, stopping at another shanty, no more than a hovel. I was amazed at the squalor of the poor Mexicans. Veronica had said that the Indian peasants — the campesinos — remained the poorest of the poor. Yet they had a dignity and endurance born of withstanding oppression and harsh conditions for generations. They were pleasant, almost cheerful, and treated me with a combination of respect and curiosity. After a dinner of soup and tortillas, I fell asleep on an old couch.

My spirits rose somewhat the next day. Despite the uncertainty of my future, I resolved to keep inwardly active — for Arthur's sake, if for no other reason — creating beauty in the aliveness of each moment and seeking to perceive the best in my environment.

In moments when I could be alone, I wept profusely, pouring out my anguish, guilt and longing. A rarefied mood came over my soul, almost a sanctity, though nothing pious. It was a feeling I had known in the aftermath of the deepest sorrows of my life, after the torment had passed, when only clarity, reverence, and gratitude remained. Pride had flown, arrogance dissolved. My soul was humbled, tranquil, almost serene.

Out of the emptiness new resolve was born. Something fresh, living, sacred — a will to become a part of that which I had experienced at the best moments of my life, when I had bathed in the love, kindness, and self-sacrifice of friends and family.

Perhaps it was a facet of what Arthur had called "theogeny," the stirring of the god-seed, the will to become divine. Or at least the aspiration to assist that sacred element which could only be described as godlike and compassionate — the intangible elixir of life which gave to life its meaning — some universal distillate of wisdom and love. In some vaguely defined way, I felt that THAT toward which I strived was the essence of the Divine Feminine, the mystic Sophia — what I had begun to refer to in my thinking as the Mother of the World.

The poverty of rural Mexico affected me deeply. Once, when Santos had pulled over for gas, a young mother, barely more than a girl, walked by me with her baby at her breast. Remembering Arthur's injunction to engage always in constructive deeds, I gave her a peso bill worth twenty-five dollars, a small fortune to the impoverished of Mexico. The young mother smiled as if she would burst, then ran off happily.

A cloud of resentment arose in my mind toward the medallion. Not only had it brought immeasurable distress into my life, it didn't in the least enhance my power to do good in the world. The thought then occurred to me that the relic's positive potential remained unknown. Despite my childish dabbling, I had discovered next to nothing of its secrets.

Spying an old, sickly woman seated by the road, I ambled over, clutching the medallion in my pocket. With my imagination I directed a stream of golden light into the woman's body and energy field, asking the spiritual powers to heal. I also visualized a radiant light pouring down upon her from above.

Surprisingly, the old woman sneezed violently three times, then stood up laughing. She stretched, looked at me squarely, and smiled. To my astonishment, she shuffled straight toward me. Grasping my arm, she exclaimed that an angel had touched her while she slept. Then she toddled away, chuckling to herself.

Had the medallion enhanced my prayers and healing visualizations? Or would the same result have been accomplished solely by my mental and spiritual efforts? I didn't know. Impulsively, I took the medallion out of its box and placed it around my neck. Remembering the frightening experience in the hotel, I began immediately to pray for divine guidance and protection.

Within moments I beheld a strange light above me. The light emanated a diffuse, luminous vapor. Within the mist I beheld a visage of utter loveliness — a woman's face, yet otherworldly, like no woman of earth. An inexpressible tenderness flowed from her face and eyes. It was the same glorious being of whom I had become aware while on the road to Nogales. The dazzling woman smiled at me and gestured with her delicate hand in the direction of the road.

I became aware of my surroundings again, and noticed a group of peasants hurrying by, carrying sacks of flour and goods. I was astonished to see a vivid, yellow glow around them. Within the golden light, individual colors began to appear. I could distinguish a different field of colors encircling each individual, and realized that I was perceiving the aura of each person — his or her unique thought and emotional makeup, expressed as color.

In my mind's eye, I saw the campesinos arriving that evening at a small village of grass huts, teeming with Indians. I saw them distributing the flour and food among the villagers. Two of them, a man and a woman, came to a small hut, apparently their own. There on a bed of blankets was a young girl of about four: their daughter. An elderly woman knelt sadly, soothing the child. I shuddered to perceive that the young girl, ravaged by fever, hovered near death.

Somehow I knew that her illness was due to having eaten contaminated food. I took off the medallion, put it in the silver box, and hurried over to the campesinos. Reaching into my rucksack, I withdrew the bottle of "wonder pills" Arthur had given me.

"*Para la niña,*" I insisted. "*Medicina para la niña.*" They looked at me wonderingly, as if beholding an apparition from beyond the grave. Then they thanked me and continued on their way. I watched them disappear beyond the curve in the road, then walked back to Santos' car, marvelling at the powers of the ancient medallion.

Just before dusk, we crossed from Campeche into Yucatan. A tingling sensation ran up my spine, and I felt a thrill of joy. I had reached my destination, at least in a general sense. An indefinable knowing pervaded my awareness, informing me that my destiny awaited me here. Something in the very atmosphere was familiar. Had I perhaps lived here before, in a previous life? At any rate, I was by no means out of harm's way — anything could happen.

Santos had relatives living nearby. "We are Mayans," he told me in Spanish, pride evident in his voice. We arrived in the darkness at a small village well off the tourist path, featuring grass-roofed homes built of simple mortar. Santos led me to a one-room building belonging to his family. I fell asleep on some blankets on the dirt floor, more comfortable than I'd have been in the most luxurious resort hotel in Mexico.

In the morning, Santos drove me to a small restaurant frequented by the local peasants. He explained that he had to return to his family, near Orizaba, but that he had friends here who would look after me. I was touched by his kind spirit and sincerity. Thanking him, I pressed a large peso bill into his hand — equivalent to a hundred dollars. I also traded him my rucksack for the cloth sack which he used for his belongings. Then we said farewell.

Sitting at one of the plain tables, I ordered "motulenos," a Yucatan-style omelette: eggs with fried bananas. Afterwards,

I wrote in my notebook, seeking a sense of direction for the next step. A mood of despondency crept over me, chilling as a fog, and I languished in self-pity. Life had dealt me a bad hand and I was tired of bluffing. Things had deteriorated from bad to worse. Not only was I alone, but I had no friends or shelter. Not even a destination.

At that moment I remembered the sealed envelope Arthur had handed me in Nogales before we parted ways. I snatched it from my sack, tore it open, and began to read.

Dear Jason,

It is a mistake to think that you live in your external conditions. In truth, you live in your consciousness. More precisely, you live in your heart. Make not the mistake of most who think that they dwell in this or that nation, city, mansion, house, or hovel. All of us live in our innermost thoughts, feelings, moods, and reflections. The sum of this inner life is our soul, which we create anew each day. See to it that you fashion an inner world worthy of attracting the most exalted beings. In so doing, you will never be alone, for blessed spirits of light will accompany you on your journeys, both inner and outer.

Yours always, Arthur

My gloom instantly dissolved and I wondered at Arthur's wisdom, and at the perfect timing of my reading the letter.

A dark-haired, attractive woman entered the restaurant and sat at a table across from mine. She was wearing khaki trousers and a blue blouse. Obviously a gringo, she seemed disturbingly out of place. My equanimity evaporated, replaced by alarm, for I felt certain she was there precisely because of me.

She inspected me with a level gaze, then smiled slightly. I nervously averted my eyes. Though dressed in Indian clothes, I knew I must have looked obviously like a gringo in disguise. I fervently wished I had never dyed my hair blonde. Closing my notebook, I got up clumsily from the table, feeling like an awkward teenager in the school cafeteria.

"In a hurry?" she asked. "No need to be so on my account."

I was at a loss in how to respond to her words. *"No hablo inglés,"* I said, my face turning red, aware of how ridiculous my lie must have seemed.

The dark-haired lady smiled. "At a certain point upon the soul's journey, the telling of untruths diminishes our light. Certainly it does not become the bearer of the medallion." I froze in my tracks, stunned.

"Don't be alarmed," she continued. "Perhaps I can help you take the next step. Were you not seeking guidance?"

I was overcome with the same odd feeling that I had known with Arthur when I felt he was reading my thoughts. It seemed useless to run; I had no place to hide. Dropping my sack on the concrete floor, I slumped resignedly back into my chair.

Chapter Two

SABRINA

"If you wish to live in the light
you must step out of the shadows." E.J.M.

"How did you know these things about me?" I asked, realizing I could not avoid the mysterious woman. "You must have known Arthur?"

"He was like a brother to me," the dark-haired woman answered. "He told me about you and solicited my help."

"Are you part of some secret society or something?"

"Did Arthur speak to you about such groups?"

"We spoke about the Trilateral Commission."

"Certainly you realize such societies are not all from the Trilateralist mold." The mystery woman had the trace of a smile as she spoke.

I nodded in agreement. "Arthur and I also spoke about the Mystery Schools and Brotherhoods of Light, societies of enlightened souls who seek to help mankind. And of course, there are the great Divine Beings who are willing to assist us."

"More than willing, Jason. They are eager to help, but we must invite them into our experience through the quality of our inner life and outer activities. Yes, indeed, the destiny of human beings is inextricably interwoven with the destiny of cosmic beings. And our mutual origin and destiny are profound, inscrutably profound."

I pondered her words for a moment, realizing I had more than met my match as a thinker. "So you even know my name," I said. "And what, may I ask, is yours?"

"My name is Sabrina. May I join you?" She glanced at the empty chair at my table.

"Do I have a choice?" I said, a feeling of lightness, like a soft breeze, passing over me. "But I'd prefer to get up and walk, if you don't mind."

"Excellent idea," she said. We both stood up and shook hands. I left some money on the table, picked up my sack, and accompanied the puzzling stranger outside.

Sabrina was tall, probably five feet eight inches, and she moved with the grace of a dancer. Her eyes were a deep shade of brown, her hair black as onyx. She looked as if she were thirty-five, yet something made me think she might have been closer to fifty. Her face was pretty, though not strikingly beautiful. She radiated an indefinable quality, a combination of wisdom and refinement — an elevation of mind and dignity of spirit — that gave her a commanding presence. I could imagine her walking into a crowded room and everyone immediately noticing her.

We walked to the edge of the small village where Santos had left me. Although it was still early in the day, the heat was becoming intense. That in itself I didn't mind, but the humidity of the semi-tropical Yucatan was uncomfortable. We walked beneath some trees to a path that led through open fields before disappearing into the jungle.

I learned that Sabrina was a professor of Ancient History and of Philosophy at a large east coast University. She was on sabbatical, doing research in Central and South America. I felt certain she had other connections she was keeping to herself.

"How do you like Yucatan?" Sabrina asked.

"I love it so far," I answered. "It's beautiful and mysterious. But the heat and humidity may take some getting used to."

"The wildlife also demands one's respect," Sabrina said seriously.

"I believe it," I said emphatically.

"The Yucatan still has many secrets that it has kept from the rest of the world."

"Is that right?" I asked. "What kinds of secrets?"

"Well, keep in mind that the pyramids of Chichén Itzá, Uxmal, and so on, have been discovered by European and American civilization for less than a hundred and fifty years. These are not the only ancient Mayan cities, nor are they the greatest. I'm tempted to say that after all these years, America still waits to be discovered."

"You mean there are other lost cities out there?" I asked.

Sabrina nodded. "Indeed there are. The most important ones — in South America as well. But these are mysteries even to the modern-day descendants of the Mayans and Incas. Many know of them, but not their exact locations."

"You'd think they'd have also been discovered by now," I said, skepticism in my voice. In fact, I had read for years of the persistent belief among some anthropologists and students of the ancient world that there yet remained ancient, ruined cities in the jungles of both South and Central America, remnants of lost cultures that were, in some cases, contemporaneous with those of the fabled Atlantis and Lemuria.

Sabrina stopped to tie her bootlace, then continued. "One must remember that the jungle regions are vast and impenetrable. Not only are there mountains, valleys and other natural geological obstacles, but the wildlife can be ferocious. Most importantly, these cities remain undiscovered because that is the intention of their inhabitants."

"You mean people still live there?" I asked. Sabrina nodded. "Let's suppose you had an idea where they were," I said, my curiosity growing, "and you were equipped to survive the rigors of jungle exploration; couldn't you reasonably expect to find them?"

Sabrina paused a moment. "It's hypothetically possible, but it's highly unlikely that a member of our white civilization would succeed in such a search."

"Why is that?" I asked.

"Because he'd be killed," Sabrina said, matter-of-factly.

"The Mayans learned their lesson from the Conquistadors — is that it?"

"That's right," affirmed Sabrina. "But nonetheless, one may enter these ancient cities unharmed."

"How is that?"

"It's all a matter of having the right connections, so to speak. With the proper means of introduction, anything is possible. And if one is truly ready — that is, if he's become spiritually worthy by the quality of his life — the condition of his aura is his passport." My mind was seized with a wild hope at Sabrina's words. If what she said were true, might this be the solution I was seeking?

We fell silent, admiring the lushness and variety of the vegetation. In the distance we could hear the shrill cry of monkeys. We reached the point where the trail vanished into the denser jungle. I paused, reluctant to go farther, but Sabrina pushed ahead, apparently familiar with the terrain. I had little choice but to follow.

I reflected on her statement about secret societies. It seemed apparent that she and Arthur were in some way connected to the same mysterious lodge or fraternity. I wondered if this was not some modern-day version of the ancient Mystery

Schools of which Arthur and I had spoken, and which he had told me still existed.

"You've been through a great deal, haven't you?" Sabrina asked sympathetically.

"I guess you could say that," I responded.

"What have you learned?" Her question took me by surprise.

"What do you mean, what have I learned?" I asked defensively.

Sabrina pushed aside a branch. "The purpose of experience," she said, "is to gain knowledge, insight and wisdom. Otherwise our experience has little meaning...becoming merely 'sound and fury, signifying nothing.' External events, no matter how dramatic, form the mere skeleton of our reality. We give to events their value by overcoming limitations. Life is our teacher, but only if we grow through the lessons life offers us. The knowledge, wisdom and love we gain by living are what expand our souls. For this we came to earth."

"Believe me, I'm learning a lot. But why should I tell you? I really don't even know who you are."

"Of course, you don't need to tell me anything. Don't be offended. I didn't really expect you to give me an answer. Let's just say I was being provocative in order to make a point."

"I've learned about trust, prayer, action, and purpose," I volunteered. "I've learned to think beyond what I've been taught to think. And I've learned there are some things in life so valuable that people are willing to give their lives for them."

"Very commendable. Anything else?"

"I've also learned there are times when discreet silence is better than words."

"Have you learned what it means to be the bearer of the medallion?" Again her question took me by surprise.

"No...quite frankly, it remains a complete enigma to me."

"Jason, you have very fine qualities. If I may be so bold, I would say you are on the verge of tremendous breakthroughs in your development. You have a tendency to be too easily offended. You are pulled away from your own center by what others say and do, rather than remaining within your own inner space. Don't be so reactive. Stay connected to your indwelling presence by a listening heart. Don't get pulled into other people's negativity. You know all this intellectually. If you would practice patience and positivity at all times, and refrain from over-reacting to the perceived flaws of others, you would find yourself on the threshold of an entirely new spiritual perception."

"Do you really think so?"

"I am certain. This is one of the reasons you've had to go through these ordeals. The knowledge you gain from these experiences is not primarily conceptual or intellectual. It is a knowledge of the heart and the soul, quite beyond the dimension of words, although one day you will be able to articulate these things."

"You're talking about initiation, I suppose."

"Yes, a trial by fire...the process that burns up the impurities which hide our real nature. Your experience is a microcosm of what the entire planet is going through. And this process of planetary purification is about to accelerate tremendously. You don't realize this consciously perhaps, but you yourself chose to be instrumental in helping to warn people of these coming events and of how to prepare for them. This era, the close of our century, has been awaited for many thousands of years. It is the time of global tribulation long prophesied — the initiation of the world."

I thought for a moment about what Sabrina was telling me. "What you say strikes me as being true. Already, I feel I'm not the same person I was a week ago, when I found the relic. I feel as if my perspective has changed. My inner reference point to external things is different. I also believe my heart has expanded. The thought of adding to the suffering in the world pains me deeply. I want to make my life count for something better. I want to help....to work and to serve. I also feel...." I hesitated momentarily.

"Yes, Jason?"

"I was going to say that I also feel more courageous, but that seems ridiculous. Here I am running in fear for my life, afraid even to talk to a beautiful woman who starts a conversation with me in a restaurant. Maybe all the changes aren't so good."

"Well, your specific situation has made that necessary. Your very survival has depended on your being overly cautious. But this is temporary. It's the result of your unique karma in relation to the medallion. Of that you'll learn more later."

We arrived at a clearing in the foliage, where the path opened upon a small meadow. We paused beneath the branches of a large tree. I looked at Sabrina with a mixture of admiration and wonder, amazed that someone I had known so briefly could know me almost better than I knew myself.

"How do you know all these things about me anyway? Are you telepathic? I'm sure Arthur was."

"Telepathy is really rather simple. Thought waves are continually entering our personal energy field, or aura. If our minds are clear and free from mental and emotional armoring, and all sorts of games and posturing, these thoughts make an impression on our minds, and *voilà,* we're mind-reading."

"You didn't answer my question."

"Everyone is telepathic. With some it's a latent gift. Others have developed it."

I realized I wasn't going to get a straight answer from her. "Were you and he part of the same secret organization, or something?" I asked. "I feel I have a right to know."

"Knowledge is not a right," Sabrina said forcefully. "It is something gained by effort. What makes you think you've earned this privilege?" I hesitated, surprised by her question.

"Perhaps I was mistaken," I said, a trifle confused. "Maybe I haven't yet earned it."

"You needn't demand knowledge of another. Ask it only of yourself. Each of us holds the key to wisdom...wisdom of self and wisdom of the world. We turn that key by self-effort.

The portal we enter is in our own hearts. The temple of the mysteries is closed to no one. When the soul attains the degree of serenity which produces humility, its inner eyes are opened, and it sees into dimensions of spirit."

"I didn't mean to appear arrogant," I said.

"Arrogance and pride blunt the development of the soul's inner organs of perception. However, self-confidence is a prerequisite to higher knowledge. There is nothing wrong with being insistent. In fact, little is possible without it. But it's of ourselves that we must make demands. The teacher is within."

"What am I supposed to do now? I've given up everything for the sake of this medallion. I just want to do what's right."

"When first you found it, Jason, your heart was tainted by greed. The experiences of the past week have purged your soul of much darkness. Still, there remains more for you to do. You have yet to fully appreciate the mystery that the ancient relic represents. You must expand your courage, you must expand your power — and most important — you must expand your love. Are you ready?"

Sabrina spoke with authority and strength. Her eyes were luminous. "I'm ready," I said, not knowing what to expect.

"Then be prepared to leave the ancient, worn-out conceptions of a dying world behind you. Meet me here this evening at sunset. Bring nothing with you but the medallion...and your immortal spirit." I looked at her, captivated by her words, which stirred me deeply. Then she vanished before my astonished gaze.

Chapter Three
A JUNGLE ENCOUNTER

"By facing fear are spirit warriors made;
Thus fear is naught of which to be afraid." E.J.M.

I looked around in all directions, stunned. I had often read of such feats as disappearance, teleportation, the magic of illusion, and other miracles capable of accomplishment by great Masters and Adepts. Now I had experienced it before my own eyes. But my amazement and heightened mood soon dissolved, for I realized I was quite uncertain how to get back to the village. Exploring the edge of the clearing, I looked without success for the path on which we had come. It occurred to me that I could remain there the rest of the day. I hadn't brought food or water, but Sabrina had certainly made it clear that supplies were not required.

I glanced at the sun, hoping to get a clue which direction to go, but the golden orb in its mid-day position gave no hint toward which horizon it tended. I sat down in the clearing to compose my thoughts when a demonic howl pierced the air.

I jumped to my feet, terrified. My heart raced and the skin on my neck and back turned to ice. It sounded like the cry of a great cat. My feet were frozen in absolute fear. I dared not move, nor utter a sound. I prayed that the cry might come again from a greater distance. But to my horror, I heard a second roar — as hideous and blood-curdling as the first — this time much nearer. It was coming toward me.

Then came the silence. What terror in that emptiness! Not a sound came from the jungle. No bird. No monkey. Nothing. I knew with all my heart that I was being stalked, the object of some ruthless beast of prey. I faced in the direction of the howls, searching the foliage for any sign of movement. Slowly, breathlessly, I moved into the very center of the clearing. A slight breeze blew against me and I noticed I was drenched in perspiration. There could be no doubt that I was being watched, for I was upwind from the creature's approach.

I made a supreme effort to gain command of myself. Though I had never known fright so great as this, I told myself that fear was useless. I would act with presence of mind regardless of what might come. I resolved that if I must die, torn apart by a wild beast, I would leave this world a brave man.

The underbrush to my left shook slightly, noiselessly. Into the clearing, moving silently and with a grace that was almost gentle, came a large spotted jaguar. It crept toward me, yellow eyes gleaming, head close to the ground, in the universal crouch of the cat approaching its prey. In that instant, my mental clarity was heightened, and time seemed to slow in accordance with some enigmatic principle. The moment expanded and time stopped, out of respect for the profundity of death.

We studied each other, hunter and hunted, representatives of two alien worlds. Experience and tradition had decreed that we were enemies. Still I marveled at the jaguar's wild, mottled beauty and regal magnificence. Yet another two or three steps and it would pounce. "God help me!" came the ceaseless, silent cry of my heart.

I raised my arms above my head, as if in voiceless salutation to the jaguar, and to the sun above, giver of life to us both. Some wild force rushed through me and I laughed aloud. The mad emotion released an unknown strength, and in that instant terror vanished.

I shouted with all the power of my soul. I knew from my spirit's secret depths that the life streaming through both the jaguar and me issued from the same unfathomable Source. We each had our origins in God.

Hate dissolved along with fear. Love filled my being, a love for life itself. Though in an instant I would die, never had I felt so intensely, joyously alive. Though my limbs and heart be torn asunder, my soul would rise unscathed into regions of eternal light.

The jaguar raised its head slightly, coming out of its crouch. It sauntered around me in a circle, then with a mild growl, loped off into the foliage from whence it had come. I laughed again, my spirit soaring to new heights of happiness and joy. Sensing the direction of the village, I ran into the underbrush, carefree, jubilant, free!

Chapter Four
THE ENCHANTRESS

"In every affair consider what precedes and what follows." —Epictetus

That evening, I awaited Sabrina in the small clearing. The sun descended beneath the trees, and the gathering twilight gave birth to the first, faint star. I lay upon my back, listening to the sounds of the jungle, watching the stars appear one by one against the satin sky.

My celestial observations were interrupted by the rustle of footsteps. I saw the light of a lantern approaching and arose to greet Sabrina.

"Hello Jason," came a soft voice — a woman's, but not Sabrina's.

"Hello," I answered. "Where's Sabrina?"

"She'll be along soon, but she's been delayed. She sent me to keep you company. I am Celeste." The woman reached out her hand in the darkness. Her garments were illumined by the lantern. She wore a traditional white skirt and blouse typical of Mayan women of the region. She spoke beautiful English with a slight Spanish accent.

Setting the lantern on the ground, Celeste unrolled a tent and deftly set it up, refusing my offer to assist her. Then she asked me to clear the ground to build a fire. Within a few minutes, flames darted toward the sky in front of the tent. Celeste spread a large, colorful blanket on the ground between the tent and the campfire and we sat down upon it.

The situation struck me as odd, for it did not seem like Sabrina to be late — especially after her dramatic departure that day. I decided I would hold my questions until later.

"Sabrina tells me you are the bearer of the medallion," Celeste announced. I was taken completely by surprise.

"Did she, really?" I asked. "I would've thought she'd be more discreet."

"Don't worry," Celeste said, laughing. "You can trust me. Sabrina has complete confidence in me."

"I'm glad to hear that," I said, not knowing what to make of this bizarre twist. "Do you live around here?" I asked, trying awkwardly to develop the conversation.

"Yes, in a general sense. That is, I live in the Yucatan peninsula." She gestured with her hand toward the surrounding jungle.

"May I ask what line of work you're in?" My question seemed painfully clumsy. Celeste laughed loudly. There was something strong and appealing about her.

"I am a shaman," she answered, matter-of-factly.

"How wonderful!" I responded. "I mean, that must be so fascinating. Shamanism is making quite a comeback these days." Celeste was silent. I was beginning to feel like an idiot.

"May I see it?" she asked calmly.

"See what?" I said.

"The relic."

"I...I suppose there's no harm in it." I slowly removed the talisman from my pocket, puzzled by the unexpected request. Celeste reached out and grabbed the medallion from me. I stared at her suspiciously.

"It's so beautiful!" she said, examining it closely by the light of the fire. "What strong magic it has! What have you accomplished with it?"

"Why, nothing really. I mean...mostly I've just tried to prevent other people from taking it." Celeste laughed even more loudly.

"But Jason, don't you realize what you have? This is the Medallion of Isis...the greatest and most powerful talisman of the ancient world. Why, with the medallion's power you could have whatever you desire. Didn't Arthur tell you? The bearer of this amulet has the power to gain world dominion if that is what he wants. But you must first be able to tap into its power. Just look!"

Celeste thrust the lustrous relic into my face, pointing at the curious hieroglyphs on the back and front.

"These are words of power, kept secret from the foolish and profane. Could you but decipher and pronounce these sounds, a host from the unseen world would appear to do your bidding. But even the glyphs themselves contain great power. Watch!"

Celeste took a stick and thrust it in the flames. When the end became hot, she withdrew it and began to write in the dirt, chanting almost inaudibly beneath her breath. As she scrawled the ancient symbol upon the earth, the curling smoke from the stick began to expand and take shape. Before my startled gaze, a host of wraith-like phantoms appeared. They gradually joined to create one form — that of a beautiful, almost tangible woman. Her garments were those of an Egyptian priestess.

I inhaled some smoke from the fire and fell into a mild, half-conscious revery. From my dream-like trance I heard Celeste command boldly. "Gold! At once bring gold!" Then I passed out.

When I recovered some minutes later, Celeste sat beside me, a look of triumph on her face. On the blanket at my feet lay a dazzling gold coin, apparently ancient. Reaching down, I inspected it closely. On one side was the Egyptian hawk, Horus — on the other, the face of a ruler, possibly a pharaoh.

"Do you see?" cried Celeste. "What awesome magic the medallion contains! Watch again!" She drew another glyph in the dirt, this time with her finger, again chanting incomprehensibly. Instantly, the flames of the fire took on a greenish tint, then turned brilliant gold, then red, blue and violet. The violet flames condensed into a screen. Images began to appear upon it. I saw scenes from ancient history dance before my eyes — first Egyptian, then Greek, Roman, Medieval, and on into the modern era. Celeste moved her hands over the violet screen, and as she did so, the images moved faster or slower, according to her will.

"Do you understand, Jason? Knowledge! All knowledge at your fingertips. The medallion is profound. Will you not use it with me? Let us together share its power!"

Celeste stood up, leaving the relic resting upon the blanket. She loosened her skirt and peeled off her blouse. Beneath her traditional garments she wore a red silk gown. Tossing aside her Mayan garb she twirled around, dancing seductively. The thin silk hugged her young, bronze body, revealing the moon-like contours of her youthful beauty.

She gracefully encircled the fire and gently sat beside me, placing her strong, yet delicate, hand on mine.

"Won't you come with me, Jason? Together we shall reign as king and queen. No harm can come upon us. We would know riches and power. Oh, Jason," she said, infinite sweetness in her voice, "we would know love!" She leaned her face toward mine, her eyes shining with tender passion.

My mind spun crazily, my heart pounded. I was dazzled by her beauty, and by the spectacle of the medallion's powers.

Uncertainty filled my soul like a fog. I thought of my friends and loved ones, of Melissa and Angelina — and of the danger in which I had placed them. I thought of all I had endured to get to this point. The image sprang to mind of the Shrine of Our Lady in Mexico City. In a flash, I saw Arthur, medallion in hand, clutch his heart and fall.

"No!" I said flinging away her hand. "I can't betray them. I can't let them down!" I seized the relic and stood up, kicking violently at the fire. "Why are you tormenting me?" I shouted, turning to face Celeste.

The fire had turned to smoldering embers, and there was no one on the blanket. The enchantress had disappeared into the jungle as mysteriously as she had appeared. I felt immediately dizzy and faint; a powerful swoon eclipsed my consciousness. I stumbled into the tent and passed out.

Chapter Five
THE SHAMAN

"Divine Law has decreed and does maintain,
'Tis in the act of giving that we gain." E.J.M.

I awoke the next morning from a dreamless sleep, feeling alert and refreshed. Stepping from my tent, I saw Sabrina seated on the blanket beside the remains of the fire.

"Good morning, Jason," she said.

"Morning," I responded. "You're late."

"Yes, Jason. Under normal circumstances, I should apologize. But it was necessary that I...well...make myself scarce, as they say. Don't take it personally, but perhaps you now realize that much is demanded of those who seek the eternal wisdom."

"Maybe too much!" I said.

"You've won my admiration," Sabrina continued. "You conducted yourself with distinction."

"I suppose that means I passed."

"These matters aren't to be judged by worldly standards, nor am I in any way your judge. It is entirely between you and your own Higher Self. What is right for one individual may not be for another. But in regard to the trials you have chosen — subconsciously — to undergo, I'm permitted to say that you've almost exceeded expectations. However, too much talk on these matters only trivializes their content. They are for your personal reflection. Contemplation of the events of recent days will reap bountiful treasures for your inner life. The most important result is the steeling of your character."

"Much preferable to the 'stealing' of my medallion," I said. Sabrina smiled slightly.

"Let's be on our way," she said, hastily rising to her feet. Something about Sabrina's cool, detached manner was irritating. She was so calm, as if nothing that happened to anyone could disturb her. It was not at all what I believed compassion for the hardship of others was all about. Her aloofness bothered me.

"You sure don't feel much sympathy for other people's suffering," I said abruptly. "Nothing seems to faze you." Sabrina hesitated a moment. A light flashed in her eyes, but a shadow crossed her face.

"Would you prefer me to show more emotion?" she said coolly.

"Why can't this damn spiritual stuff have more passion?" I said. "I mean, I go through the most difficult experiences of my life, then have all these tests and trials, and you give me a pat on the head and act as though it's no big deal...as if nothing much has happened."

"Did I give you that impression?" Sabrina said. Her indifference was almost maddening.

"Look, I'm sorry," I said. "I guess I'm just a hot-head. You are a professor, an academic. My path has been so different. You don't have a family...no children...you've probably never been married. I guess it's easier for you to be detached."

Sabrina was silent. She gazed at the remains of the fire, a faraway look in her eyes. Her expression for an instant appeared almost downcast. It occurred to me that my thoughts were not concealed from her.

"What makes you think I've never had those experiences, Jason?"

I felt abruptly chastened. "I guess I'm presuming a lot. I'm sorry." I realized I was accusing her of being insensitive, but I was the one actually lacking in understanding. Sabrina smiled slightly. Her eyes were like two brilliant stars. For the first time, I saw the depth of love in her heart.

"Do you have a family?" I asked. "I shouldn't have assumed anything."

Sabrina reflected momentarily. "It's not something I had intended to share with you, Jason. But you may find it helpful to know that I was once married and had a delightful daughter, a charming three-year-old, a bundle of heavenly love...much like your precious Angelina." A lump formed in my throat. Her use of the past tense sent a chill through me.

"Divorce, I suppose," I said quietly, afraid there was more to it than that.

Sabrina hesitated. Her face became soft, her features tender. "No, not that. My husband and daughter...." She paused for what seemed an eternity. "My husband and daughter both died in a fire that destroyed our home." I was stunned. Shattered. Tears came to my eyes and I clenched my teeth.

"I...I'm so sorry," I stammered. "Please forgive me. I've been such a fool."

There was a long pause. "It's nothing you could have known," Sabrina said. "It's been fifteen years now." Her voice was little more than a whisper. "A part of one never recovers. Yet by going through that hellish tragedy, my heart was opened to the realities of heaven." I bowed my head in silence.

In the hush that followed, I was overcome with remorse for my foolish words and baseless assumptions. My respect for Sabrina was boundless.

"You see, Jason, when the very worst that could possibly happen to a person *actually happens,* she has a choice. She can become bitter...and begin to shrivel and die inside. Or she can rise above her grief and sorrow, and be reborn into a higher, more compassionate and love-filled existence. If she ascends to this second birth — this spiritual awakening in the heart — the quality of her emotional experience will never be the same."

She stood up and rapidly dismantled the tent. "I see you took me in earnest...about travelling lightly." Her cheerful words broke the awkward silence.

"Well, I wasn't sure if I should take you literally," I replied softly. I was thoroughly, deeply chastened. "But I left my things with Santos' family...the fellow who brought me here."

"You won't be needing any of it," said Sabrina. She had a heavenly expression in her eyes. I realized that resentment was something entirely alien to her character. In my own clouded judgment, I had interpreted her tranquility of spirit to be insensitivity. I resolved never to judge someone by appearances again.

Sabrina reached into her backpack and pulled out a pair of black boots, similar to the ones she was wearing.

"No need to suffer unduly, however," she said, handing them to me, along with a pair of socks. Then she gave me some concentrated food, slightly sweet, which I ate as we began our journey through the jungle.

"May I ask where we're going?" I asked, relieved to be once more on our way.

"That's one of the most profound philosophical questions one may ever ask," Sabrina said playfully. She had entirely dismissed the incident by the campfire.

"I didn't mean it in an ultimate evolutionary sense...for heaven's sake!" Thanks to Sabrina's nobility of spirit, my own spirits were rising again.

"Pardon me for being mysterious," she said. "But be patient. You'll find out soon enough." Realizing I wouldn't get any more information from her, I resigned myself to relax and enjoy the journey.

Other than Sabrina's machete, most of the few items we brought with us were in her backpack. I carried the tent in its pouch, and we each had a canteen of water. The jewelled relic remained within its silver case in my pocket. I dared not place it around my neck, even with Sabrina by my side.

The jungle was thick and close, but Sabrina soon led us to a trail that was passable. Regarding the ever-present wildlife, she told me to practice kinship with all life. "Be mindful and cautious of potentially harmful creatures," she said, "but fear is useless and dangerous." In the aftermath of my encounter with the jaguar, I felt an inner confidence and lightness of being previously unknown to me.

"About the jaguar..." I said. "Was I really on my own, or would you have protected me in some way?"

"If necessary," she answered, "I would have intervened to protect you."

"Next time," I said, "I'd much prefer knowing that beforehand."

Sabrina smiled and winked. "Maybe I just enjoy watching you squirm."

After travelling without a break for several hours, we stopped briefly to rest atop a large outcropping of rocks on the side of a hill. Our food was exclusively the slightly sweet concentrate provided by Sabrina. She pointed out a cluster of grass huts, or palapas, almost camouflaged by the surrounding jungle. I had noticed earlier how much cooler and more comfortable the grass palapas were compared to the mortar ones I'd been in. Many Indians now aspired to build their huts of concrete because they had more status than the grass ones, but at the sacrifice of temperature comfort. Even they were not immune to modern pressure for "progress," regardless of cost.

To my amazement, I heard a popular Mexican song wafting through the air, followed by a commercial extolling the virtues of a Mexican soft drink.

"The global mass culture is everywhere, my friend," Sabrina said, almost with dismay. "Most of these Indians speak no Spanish. And though they have no electricity, telephones and so forth, they do have some battery-powered tools and radios. The voice of consumerism is omnipresent."

"It's a shock...in such a remote area."

"These people mix with the modern culture when they choose," Sabrina explained, "but prefer to remain isolated. There are not many like them left, but in the near future, the indigenous lifestyle of the native peoples will experience a rebirth. The new Indian culture of the Americas which shall rise, phoenix-like, in the coming years, will be better than the pre-Columbian civilization. We tend to romanticize the lost Native American cultures, but they weren't perfect."

"But at least they lived in harmony with the earth and the natural kingdoms," I said. "I think we have a lot to learn from the native cultures."

"No argument there. The world has a tremendous debt of gratitude to the Indians of America. And that's not just for the material gifts they gave to the world, such as potatoes, yams, tomatoes, squash, corn, chocolate and so forth. Their love of the earth and nature is a beautiful, powerful bond...a profound spiritual kinship. They appreciate that the earth is a living being."

I looked out across the impressive jungle panorama. "How did the modern world become so insensitive to the earth as animate and living?" I asked. "Is Christianity to blame?"

Sabrina reflected quietly for some moments before answering. "Christianity today stands at a historic interlude or transition point," she began. "Much of modern Christianity has drifted away from its mystical roots and cosmic origins. When dogma replaces direct insight, religion often becomes the blind leading the blind. Without spiritual vision, orthodoxy becomes an empty shell. In the coming age, Christianity will be re-united with the stream of cosmic wisdom known as the Mysteries.

"Despite its failings," she continued, "historical Christianity is not the culprit responsible for the current destruction of nature. From the fall of Rome through the Middle Ages, Europe was almost entirely permeated by Christianity, in spirit if not always in practice. It's not for nothing they called it 'Christendom.' During that era there was ignorance in many areas, but nature was not violated. In fact, Natura, as she was called, was endowed with living qualities. Nature was recognized as a Being of beauty, majesty and power...commanding and deserving respect. Christianity's true relationship to nature is best emblemized in the example of St. Francis and his great love for all creatures. What really blunted this perception, and changed people's relationship to nature, was the birth of scientific materialism, leading gradually to the Industrial Revolution."

"It's a sad part of history, in my opinion," I said. "The birth of the factories led to a mass migration from the rural farms to the crowded, industrial cities."

"Sad, but perhaps necessary," Sabrina commented. "Commercialism, as we know it today, was born. With the technological applications of material science came a loss of spiritual perception, and the gradual toxification of the earth. In our times, this is a crisis of staggering proportions. The modern world's greed and exploitation of nature has been spawned by the commercial misdirection of materialistic science."

Sabrina stood up and put on her backpack. Feeling refreshed, we descended from the cluster of boulders and approached the remote Indian village. We came to a cluster of grass huts, more primitive than most I had seen.

Several Indian children greeted Sabrina, whom they obviously knew. A middle-aged woman ran out to welcome us, sporting a toothless grin. She escorted the two of us into one of the huts where an old man sat on a straw mat upon the earthen floor. He wore a shirt made of jaguar skin and plain, blue pants rolled up at the cuff. He looked at us and nodded, smiling at Sabrina. The two of them spoke in a language I could not understand. I presumed the old man spoke no Spanish.

He stood up and took a step toward me. "What's happening, dude?" he said to me, grinning broadly. Then he and Sabrina burst out laughing. My mouth dropped when I heard him speak colloquial American slang.

"This is Chilam," Sabrina said, controlling her amusement. "He's got quite a sense of humor." Chilam beamed at me, his eyes twinkling.

"He speaks English?" I asked in amazement.

"A little," said Sabrina. "You'd be surprised to know how much he understands. Chilam is really very remarkable." She paused, then added, "Why don't you show him the medallion?" I hesitated, then removed the relic from my pocket. Chilam began carefully examining the relic, making sounds of sincere admiration.

He stared deeply into my eyes, smiled, and spoke some incomprehensible words to Sabrina. The two of them chuckled together, apparently enjoying a laugh at my expense.

"He says your head's too big for your shoulders," Sabrina explained. "You think you're a great shaman, but you still have a long way to go."

"Me? Right now I don't think I'm much of anything."

"I will help you," Chilam said to me in Spanish. He motioned for us to follow and we traipsed behind him into the green forest.

After walking about a hundred yards, we came upon a small, rapidly flowing stream. Chilam knelt and put his hand in the water, then stood up and stared at me.

"You have a family?" he asked me.

"Yes, my wife and my daughter."

"Lovely," he said, smiling. "Pretty little girl. She's almost four, no?" I nodded, figuring there was absolutely nothing I could hide from these people.

"Please give me the picture," Chilam demanded.

"What picture?" I said defensively.

"The picture of your family. I must take it." I was astonished that he knew I had a photo of my wife and daughter, the last vestige of my old life, now so far away. I kept it in laminated plastic, tied by a string to my underpants. It was my only memento of my loved ones — my last remaining personal possession.

"But why?" I protested. "I've given up everything else. Can't I just keep this? Please!" I looked at Sabrina for support, but she stared at the ground impassively.

Chilam was unbending. "The spiritual adventurer," he said, "must not be tied down to anything of earth. He must be able to let all of it go, if necessary. Nothing of the world may have power over us. Nothing."

Reluctantly I reached into my black pants and untied the laminated photo. I took one last look at it, engraving the image into my mind. A wave of sadness swept over me.

"Cherish them in your heart," Chilam said, putting his left hand gently on my shoulder. "There they can never leave you, but will stay in your soul forever." Chilam touched his heart with his right hand. Then he took the photo, knelt beside the stream, and placed it face up in the flowing water. We watched in silence until the current carried it from view behind a bend.

Chilam looked at me sympathetically. "Happiness doesn't come from externals," he continued. "It is a condition of the soul. States of feeling exist separately from physical objects. We Indians have learned not to mistake the two. Learn to cultivate the desired feelings, then you will realize you don't need material objects. Ironically, you will then also discover that the physical things will come to you more easily, not in order to possess, but to enjoy."

"The secret of receiving," said Sabrina, as we turned and walked away from the stream, "lies first in giving. The only things we keep are those we first give away. When we act, the universe reacts. This is the law of causation, or karma. What comes to you is the result of what you have given, either through service, or perhaps as an actual gift. That which enters your experience is directly equated to the causes you set in motion by the action of head, heart, and hand. As a result, the more you give of that which is beneficial and helpful, the more you receive."

"I once read," I said, my mental clarity returning, "that in India they have a saying, 'what isn't given is lost.'"

"That's a beautiful expression," said Sabrina, "and it's true. The hand that gives, gathers."

"We don't have to give up things themselves," I said. "Only our emotional enslavement to them. Isn't that what you're saying?"

"Exactly," answered Sabrina. "In fact, when we live the law of giving, we find that we open ourselves to receive in such bountiful measure that we can scarcely deal with the harvest. Give freely, and freely you will receive. Receiving is the effect of giving. You can take out of your life only what you've put into it. Give, and it shall be given unto you. Apply this law of causation in every life circumstance and you will become a master of your destiny."

By this time we had reached Chilam's little hut. Chilam motioned for us to go inside, then he disappeared into the forest. Sabrina and I made ourselves comfortable on the grass mats.

Chilam returned moments later, carrying some herbs, bark, and leaves. He busied himself preparing a beverage which he insisted I drink. It was slightly bitter, with a salty aftertaste.

"Made from tree bark," said Chilam.

"It's in the quinine family," added Sabrina. "It will strengthen your resistance to illness or infection here in the jungle." Chilam also gave me some roots to chew on, to prevent stomach disorders of the type to which all gringos are prone.

We sat for a time in silence. Chilam was brooding deeply, a grave expression etched on his features. "The world must learn from the Indians," he said, peering seriously into my eyes. "Our continent has been conquered, but not our soul. Modern civilization is on the verge of destroying the earth. You must learn from the Indians before it's too late." I was riveted by his intensity.

"Learn from our knowledge of nature, kinship with the animal life, and our insight into the healing and medicinal powers of plants. You think that a weed is an enemy that must be killed so your lawns will be green. But a weed is a being with an intelligence. Behind it is an entity, what you would call a nature spirit or deva. It has a reason for existing. All things play a part in the economy of nature. One day you will realize that what you call weeds are often great healers. Each is a doctor, a nurse, waiting to help. In the future, all medicines will come from what you today call weeds, as well as other plants. Every plant, even the toxic, have a use."

Chilam grew visibly sad. "There is little time," he said. "Your people must learn to love the earth and all creatures, for Nature is the garment of God. Your commercialism, your corporations....your pollution and greed...these are endangering the very life of the planet. You must tell your brothers and sisters to stop. Do you not see? The soul of the planet is being destroyed."

Chilam spoke earnestly, and I was moved by his quiet, passionate plea. I was at a loss for words, but felt somehow personally responsible for the destruction of nature. "I'm sorry," I said. Chilam smiled and patted my ankle. He stood up, and Sabrina and I did likewise. Chilam shook my hand — then walked softly into the forest.

"It's time to go," Sabrina said, picking up her things. The old shaman was nowhere to be seen.

"I wanted to thank him," I said.

"Don't worry. He's got his own inscrutable manner of divining your gratitude."

I plucked a large, red jungle flower and left it on the mat where I first saw Chilam seated. Then we gathered our few things and started into the jungle.

We trekked for more than an hour before coming to a rushing river, not far from an impressive waterfall. Sabrina led me along some dry rocks to the edge of the falls. We took off our boots and she motioned me to follow her.

We passed behind the falls, stopping to listen to the crashing water. The sound was entrancing; I was mesmerized by the pristine beauty of the elements, so perfectly and harmoniously blended. I closed my eyes and soon was lost in contemplation.

When I opened my eyes, Sabrina was no longer beside me. I suppressed a feeling of mild irritation, then started walking behind the falls, attempting to reach the other side of the river. But to my dismay, the path behind the waterfall narrowed until it disappeared in the crashing water. I had no choice but to return the way I had come. Stepping on the dry stones, I reached the embankment and clambered to the top.

I put on my boots and paced back and forth, calling Sabrina's name — at first hesitantly, then at the top of my lungs. There was no response. I was more chagrined than puzzled, feeling certain she was playing some game to test me. "Steeling my character," I said half-aloud. Kneeling on the shore, I pondered my next move.

"*Venga aqui*. Come this way," said a voice from across the stream. I looked up, surprised to see Chilam standing in the water a few feet from the river's edge. He motioned for me to cross the stream in front of him. I took off my boots, tied them together, and slung them over my shoulder. I stepped in the water and began to cross the swirling current.

Chilam also waded further into the river, and as I approached midstream, he stood just an arm's length away. Extending his hand, he spoke calmly. "Be careful, my son, it gets deep." I thought it odd he should say that, for I was barely a yard from him, and the water was only slightly above our waists.

Taking a step, I reached for his hand. But my foot never touched bottom. I fell in over my head, and sank several feet before kicking up towards the surface. I could see the light just above me, but before my head broke the surface, Chilam's strong hand pressed against my crown, preventing me from rising. I was stunned, thinking for a second that he had accidentally pushed me down. I rose again, extending my arm towards the top. He shoved down even harder and I struggled to break free. Chilam was drowning me.

I kicked and fought with all my strength, but Chilam gripped my collar with one hand and with the other pressed hard in my face. His strength was terrifying. I struggled furiously, then floundered, my heart overcome by a sense of betrayal. I had been lured by Sabrina and Chilam deep into the forest to be murdered.

My lungs burned with a torturous fire. My head seemed ready to explode. Before me yawned a cavernous blackness. I could fight no longer.

There was an explosion of light all around me. Instantly, the horrible sensations of suffocation were extinguished. I was not aware of my body — only the blinding luminosity.

The light diminished and I found myself in a twilight world of soft light and soothing color. The sounds of sweet music, like that of harmonic chimes, sounded in my ears. All at once, I became aware of a tunnel moving towards me. I was overcome with curiosity and a desire to explore the tunnel, which lured me with a sense of familiarity, as if I were going home. Instantly, I was propelled into the tunnel, the chimes still tinkling sweetly.

I whooshed through the tunnel and found myself walking in a beautiful garden, filled with all manner of delightful flowers and exotic plants. Later I remembered in particular the fragrance of roses and freesias.

There appeared before me a tall Being, clothed in a scintillating white robe. From her countenance streamed ineffable loveliness, kindness and gentle feeling. A prismatic radiance streamed from the head of the luminous Being, expanding outward in all directions, giving the impression of wings formed of rainbow light. The Shining One was the most resplendent creature I had ever seen. Her eyes were diamonds of living light, and gazed at me with indescribable tenderness. Surely I had died, and was encountering an angel on the inner planes of reality.

The Shining One took a step closer to me. Instantly, images of my entire life began to stream past my awareness in a pictorial, almost cinematic, panorama from earliest childhood to that very day. I saw all my actions played out before me, those motivated by selfishness, and those inspired by kindness.

The times I had made people feel happy and when I had hurt them. But I felt not my own feelings at the time, but what my actions had caused others to experience.

I saw myself as a teenager, angry at my younger brother for not wanting to play in a sandlot baseball game, leaving our team shorthanded. I saw myself hit him repeatedly, until he began to cry. I felt his humiliation and pain, and was overcome with shame at my cowardly, bullying behavior.

The imagery of the years passed and I beheld my recent actions toward Melissa. I saw myself dash to pieces our precious wedding china, then seize my daughter's tiny chair, hurling it furiously onto the patio, damaging it permanently. I could feel Melissa's sorrow and hurt.

My life review continued right up to my escape into Yucatan. I felt the joy of the young Indian mother, baby at her breast, when I handed her the money. And the happiness of the campesino family, to whom I'd given Arthur's anti-toxin pills, as their young daughter began to recover from her close scrape with death.

The Shining One did not speak, yet I heard a voice in my mind. "Death is the soul's rebirth into the heavenly regions from whence it has come...its true and everlasting home. I am always with you, from birth until death, and then again on into another embodiment, ever recurring.

"Life is precious, each moment an opportunity. Waste not your allotted time on earth. We ever guide and protect you. But we respect your free will. You must reach out to us consciously, of your own volition. Grow toward us in stature. It is through love that you grow. If you acknowledge our presence, you will never lack our assistance. Your time, little one, has not yet come. To earth you must fall again. We await you when your work is accomplished. Do not falter; we are by your side."

A surge of love flowed like a current from the radiant Being's heart to my own. I felt such bliss, such sweet happiness, in the Shining One's presence that I did not want to return to my body. I knew with all my heart that death, when it called me, would be a joyful liberation, so long as my life had been honorably lived.

The Shining One's image began to fade and I seemed to fall backwards, through the tunnel, pausing for an instant in the twilight world of soft lights and colors. Then this world also faded.

When I regained consciousness in my body, I was resting upon the opposite bank of the river, my head gently cradled in Chilam's arms. He pressed a warm cup of tea to my lips. Sabrina knelt beside me, caressing my hand.

"Praise be unto the Great Spirit of Life," said Chilam. "Sacred is this moment, my son, for you have beheld, face to face, your blessed guardian angel. Never shall you be without her companionship, lest you sever the bond. Peace be with you. Now drink and regain strength. Your life has been blessed beyond measure."

He put the cup to my lips again and I drank it down, feeling vital force stream through my limbs. Slowly, with Sabrina's help, I rose to my feet.

Chapter Six
LINKS WITH THE PAST

"There are more things in heaven and earth, Horatio,
than are dreamt of in your philosophy."
—William Shakespeare

Sabrina, Chilam and I stood on a rock atop a high ridge, overlooking a vast stretch of emerald green — as far as the eye could see. The sky was a shimmering, pale blue, entirely void of clouds. Throughout the day, I had remained engrossed in contemplation of my profound experience, in awe of the marvels I had been permitted to behold. We sat in silence watching the crimson sun sink below the trees. As the creeping shadows of twilight engulfed us, Sabrina and I set up her tent and built a fire, while Chilam went to gather herbs.

The fire danced and flickered in Sabrina's eyes when at last she broke the silence. "Angels are divine messengers," she began. "They are not upon the human life wave, but rather the devic, from the Sanskrit word, 'deva,' meaning 'shining one.' They are indeed glorious, emanating an indescribable light, as you now know by personal experience. Nature spirits, gnomes, sylphs, fairies, sprites, and so forth, are upon this line of evolution, paralleling that of the human. The fairies and nature spirits are the little brothers and sisters of the angels. After long eons of development, they too shall become angelic."

"Does everybody have a guardian angel?" I asked.

"Each human being is assigned a guardian angel at the beginning of that soul's sojourn into the material worlds, and the angel stays with it through countless incarnations, ever there to assist if called upon. Until the human being is able to gain control of his emotional nature, the angels cannot come too close. But as the individual ascends in stature and development, the angel may draw very near, providing inspiration, guidance and divine illumination."

"What's the difference between the angel and the spirit guide?" I asked, tossing a stick on the fire.

"The spirit guide is a human being with more wisdom than we ourselves have, who works in the capacity as teacher on the inner planes of life. Our guide performs a service by assisting us in many ways in our daily life. She will inspire, and at times even give us practical assistance from the other side, smoothing out material difficulties in a manner of which humans are unaware. But she can never do our work for us, nor interfere with our karma. Do not confuse the angel with the spirit guide. An angel, as a rule, has never been a human being."

"I'm aware that there are many kinds of angels," I said. "Are some more evolved than others?"

The light of the fire cast Sabrina's shadow against the nearby trees. "Oh yes, indeed," she answered. "There is an incredible variety of divine, spiritual life — right on up to the highest Being the mind of man may contemplate. Although orthodoxy cringes at the thought, the highest Gods themselves are still evolving. Even the angels may learn from the more advanced human beings."

"So even the angels and archangels are still growing," I said.

"All of life continually progresses. To do otherwise would be stagnation...something not within the divine scheme. There are many orders and ranks of angels. Most people have heard of angels and archangels, but this is only the beginning. There are nine main levels in all. The most exalted of these are almost beyond human comprehension. It is helpful, in imagining the stature of these beings, to consider that all the stars and planets are the physical bodies of great Spiritual Beings.

"The spiritual life is highly organized. All that happens on earth is noted and recorded. The higher ethers are composed of light-sensitive substance that records every thought, word, and deed. These are the so-called Akashic Chronicles, or God's Book of Remembrance."

"I guess there's no place to hide."

"None at all, although many try to hide, even from themselves." Sabrina poked the fire with a stick.

"In addition to the divine angels who assist human beings," she continued, "there are the great men and women who have reached an advanced stature, having completed the stages of higher initiation. These are the Masters, the great teachers and Elder Brothers. They are part of the exalted Brotherhoods of Light, a vast company of perfect and nearly perfect souls."

"Where does shamanism fit into this scheme?" I asked.

"Shamanism," Sabrina said, "is one of the oldest expressions of religious striving in the world, and is rooted in the spiritual awareness of all the indigenous peoples. The word 'shaman' means 'one who sees in the dark,' in the Tungusic language of Siberia. The true shaman is a bridge between the heaven worlds and human experience, and between the nature kingdoms and mankind. Thus the tree is often a symbol of the shamanic path. Its roots represent unity with nature, while its branches extend into the celestial regions. The trunk represents the human world, poised in balance between heaven and earth."

"But it appears," I said, "that some shamanic practices are anything but elevated. I mean, more than a few shamans get stuck in low-level sorcery, doing battle against their enemies, both human and spiritual. It seems a long way from the ideal of 'love one another.'"

"It depends on the individual shaman's stage of moral and spiritual development," Sabrina explained. "In other words, there are different levels or degrees of attainment."

Sabrina put a pot of water on the coals, then tossed some herbs in the water for tea. "Traditional shamanism," she continued, "deals with the awakening of paranormal talents and engaging in the healing arts. The shaman is called to his vocation through experiencing a severe illness, perhaps because only in that way can he or she have compassion for the sickness of those who come for help. The shaman enters into visionary, ecstatic trances, employing various rituals. And he or she becomes intimately involved with supernatural dimensions interpenetrating nature. But there is a world of difference within these parameters between the lowest and loftiest forms of shamanism."

"Is that where psychedelics come in?" I asked.

Sabrina nodded. "In the lower shamanism," she explained, "the shaman often resorts to using plant psychedelics to achieve seership, or vison. Even then the vision is usually limited to the lower spiritual realms — what the Greeks called the 'nether worlds' — and which are often described in esoteric literature as the lower astral regions. These regions are close to the earth...even beneath the surface of the physical earth in some cases. Many such shamans spend a good deal of time struggling against human or spirit adversaries. Some shamanic societies are quite violent, engaging in bitter feuds and rivalries. You're right. It's almost sorcery."

"What about the higher forms?" I asked.

"In the higher shamanic practices," responded Sabrina, "the healer does not, in most instances, need psychedelics to trigger his seership, or altered state. He enters into a conscious clairvoyance of the spiritual regions through prayer, chanting, ritual, fasting, and other forms of preparation. Traditionally, most shamans use drumming to assist them in achieving an altered state. But one's character and moral development are ultimately the keys which open the portal to this higher shamanic vision, or clairvoyance. As a result, he gains the assistance of benign spiritual helpers, some animal, some human, some angelic."

Sabrina stirred the pot of water and herbs before continuing. "The shamanic tradition of certain cultures can be traced back to the influence of the Mystery Schools. This is true of the Hawaiian and Polynesian practices of the Huna. Another example is the profound healing work of the European Christian shaman, Daskalos, whose enlightened teachings have become widespread through the books of Markides."

"I find the idea of shamanic journeys fascinating," I said. "Nowadays, there are some western therapists using shamanic journeys in their healing work."

Sabrina poured some herbal tea, now boiling, into three small metal cups. "You're right. Traditionally, shamans of indigenous cultures would engage in so-called 'journeys' — involving altered states of consciousness — in order to get information helpful in their healing work, or to receive inspired knowledge. An important part of their healing involved 'soul retrieval,' or assisting patients in re-integrating a damaged and seemingly lost part of their emotional selves that had been 'driven out,' so to speak, by some life trauma. In the modern world this might be due to rape, incest, abuse, loss of a love, or some other type of personal shock."

"I know a woman," I said, "who was greatly helped by this type of shamanic healing. She was emotionally devastated when she broke up with a long-time lover. Symptomatic of her loss, her dark brown eyes turned a dull, cardboard brown and remained this way for years. In a soul retrieval session, she was able to re-capture that portion of herself which had been lost through the trauma of her break-up. A physical sign of the healing was that her eyes returned to their former deep brown lustre."

Sabrina smiled at my story. "Besides its practical application," she said, "the shamanic journey refers to the passage of Self to wholeness and completion. It is a metaphor for the individual path, the quest for self-realization and divine illumination."

I thought of the ancient Isis myth, in which the goddess had the task of reuniting the scattered portions of the body of Osiris. Perhaps the modern shamanic work of soul retrieval was symbolic of the task of the divine feminine in our times — to re-member the lost portions of our soul and spirit, damaged by the traumas of a materialistic world.

I sipped my tea, savoring the earthy blend of unfamiliar roots and herbs. "What about Chilam?" I asked.

"Chilam's over ninety years old," she said, "and is highly developed in the old Mayan system of initiation ... a secret tradition that has few practitioners nowadays. When the Spanish arrived in Mexico, the ancient Mystery tradition of the Americas was already in severe decline."

"Presumably, this includes the Aztecs," I said. "I understand their temples weren't very happy places."

Sabrina rolled her eyes. "The Aztecs were remarkable people with many admirable qualities, not the least of which were strength and determination. According to legend, the original Aztecs were imprisoned by their enemies on an island infested with venomous snakes — roughly where Mexico City is today — and left to die. But the enterprising Aztecs survived by hunting the snakes for food. They grew to be a dominant force in ancient America, displaying a genius for building and architecture.

"Sadly for the common people, the initiate knowledge of the Aztec priesthood and ruling class declined to the wretched state where they practiced human sacrifice on an abominable scale. They believed the sun was dying, and that to prevent that from happening, the sun needed to be appeased by human blood offerings. As dishonorable as the methods were that the Conquistadors used, they did the world a service by putting an end to the reign of the Aztec priests. The negative karma of the Aztec empire itself decreed that it be destroyed. Some of the old thought-forms and malicious spiritual entities, or elementals, which were created by their sacrificial rituals, plague the Americas even today.

"In fact," continued Sabrina, "much purification of the psychic atmosphere still needs to take place. It may be necessary for natural cataclysms to do some of the work."

I wasn't sure what she meant at the time, but was later to recall vividly her words.

"What about the Mayans?" I asked. "Most of their descendants are so peaceful and gentle."

Sabrina thoughtfully sipped her tea. "That's true," she said. "And the gentleness of their ancestors was one of the reasons for their spiritual greatness, for gentleness removes inner obstacles to soul perception, and stimulates the flowering of the spiritual organs, or chakras."

"It seems a paradox to be gentle," I said, "and at the same time bold and fearless."

"Perhaps this is why so many men have trouble expressing their spirituality, Jason. Oddly enough, some think gentleness is a sign of weakness." I winced, trying not to take her comment personally.

"As you know," Sabrina continued, "the inner journey is full of paradox. But what you described is the essence of the spiritual warrior. The Mayans possessed an advanced metaphysical culture. They had an amazing perception of the qualities of time, and of life rhythms and cycles."

"I've read about their calendar," I said, "and their vision of the end of the age — what's been called the Harmonic Convergence."

"They had many divisions and cycles of time," explained Sabrina. "Each day of the year had a different name and a slightly different nuance, which they sought to distinguish. To the Mayans, time was an entity, worthy of the highest reverence. They appreciated that time was a living, evolutionary impulse that would carry humanity on to perfection, through a cycle of ages. Our age is a critical period. We are at the end of a grand cycle — the threshold of its completion."

"That's opposite the Aztec view," I commented, "which held that the sun was dying, bringing time to a violent end."

Sabrina nodded in agreement. "To the Mayans," she explained, "everything was conscious, alive, permeated with feeling. They possessed a sophisticated mathematical system, and believed they were in direct communication with the galactic core, receiving and interpreting messages from this universal center. The true Mayans were agents from another star system, come to earth to harmonize earth rhythms and earth time with cosmic rhythms."

"And yet," I interjected, "they had almost no technology as we know it. Not even the wheel."

"Love and wisdom do not arise from technology," replied Sabrina. "The Mayans knew that the most sophisticated tool ever created was the human body itself."

"What happened to the Mayans?" I asked. "They seem almost to have vanished from the stage of history."

"It's something of a riddle. Unfortunately, the Mayan culture declined considerably in the centuries before the arrival of the Spanish. They also began the practice of human sacrifice in the pyramid temples, albeit on a smaller scale than their Mexican neighbors. Nonetheless, this breaking of spiritual law eventually sealed their fate. They were easily overcome by the conquering Europeans.

"However, some of the Mayans never lost the purity of their religion and world view, refusing to participate in the defiled rituals of some of the leaders. The priest-initiates of this remnant divined the coming of the Spaniards and envisioned the violence that would attend their arrival. In fact, so accurate was their calendar, they knew in advance the very day that Cortez would arrive on Mexican soil. The elders among them chose to avoid contact with the coming invaders. A core group, or remnant, remains alive to this day — secluded in their jungle hideaways — nurturing the seeds of their advanced spiritual culture."

"I suppose these are the lost cities you mentioned?" I suggested. Sabrina smiled but said nothing.

By this time Chilam had returned from his forest wanderings. He joined us by the fire and began sipping his tea.

Several minutes passed without a word. I closed my eyes and listened to the symphony of jungle sounds. After a time, I began to sense a palpable, living energy behind the audible tapestry.

"It is good to listen," said Chilam softly, breaking the spell. His words were melodious. "If you learn to listen carefully, without always passing judgment, you will enter into the very heart of the creature to whom you give attention. You will begin to grow the flowers of your soul. Then all of nature will whisper to you her secrets."

Another silence followed. I pondered Chilam's words, and entered more deeply into a relaxed alertness.

"You like Yucatan?" the old shaman asked me, interrupting the stillness. I nodded.

"It's nice that you visit us again," he said mysteriously. He was looking at me curiously. "I hope you will succeed this time." I wasn't sure what he meant. I glanced at Sabrina, but she only stared at the fire.

The old shaman stood up and motioned me to do the same. "Look at the sky," he said, pointing. "Aren't the stars beautiful?" I nodded in agreement, gazing at the dazzling, diamond vault of the heavens, visible between the tree branches. I wondered what the inscrutable Chilam was driving at.

Then the old shaman touched my forehead with his thumb. At once, a brilliant light engulfed me and I became oblivious to my surroundings. I was dimly aware that my physical body was falling to the ground. I sensed that Sabrina had caught me and gently laid me upon the grass, but I was no longer in my physical shell. I rose to a great height, and noticed that the small tent and the campfire lay far beneath me. I could see a huge expanse of the semi-tropical jungle of Yucatan.

Chilam was beside me, holding my arm. But his appearance had changed. He was youthful, handsome and strong. I noticed that he wore a feathered headdress, which I gathered signified a high rank of initiation within a particular priestly or shamanic order.

After reaching a great height above the earth, we began our descent toward the jungle. Although our journey had taken only minutes at most, it was now daytime, and the sun was overhead. Soon I could discern the outline of individual trees. We hovered above some Indian villages, similar to those I had recently seen, but I knew that these were from an earlier historical period.

Then I saw a group of Spanish soldiers, Conquistadors, gathered in a cluster, talking. Nearby were three priests — Jesuits. A group of Mayan Indians stood to the side, one of them dressed in regal attire, obviously a chieftain.

I noticed a priest I had not previously seen. He walked over and began to speak to the Indians. Quietly, almost furtively, he offered them a dazzling object. I recognized the Isis Medallion!

The other Jesuits watched the action with dismay. One of them shouted to the soldiers standing nearby. The lone Jesuit tried to run with the Indians into the nearby jungle, but he was shot with a Conquistador's large-mouthed arquebus. He fell to the earth, mortally wounded.

An inner voice of wisdom spoke, and I knew that I was the Jesuit who had been killed attempting to give the Egyptian relic to the Mayan chieftain. I realized inwardly that the priest who had shouted to the soldiers was, in his present life, Brother Reynard. The officer who had shot me was none other than the Trilateralist, Ulysses Bundy.

I glanced at Chilam, hovering beside me in his youthful spirit body. He gazed at me searchingly, and I knew I had been given the privilege of witnessing my own previous embodiment as the Jesuit priest, Dante.

The shaman touched my arm and we rose high above the earth, before heading swiftly downward. It was night again and I could distinguish the tiny campfire, a flame in the darkness, from where, in present time, my out-of-body journey had begun.

We hovered above the tent, then my surroundings vanished in a blinding flash. The light diminished swiftly and I knew myself to be once more in my fleshly form. I made an effort to rise, but fell back, soundly sleeping, my head upon a grassy pillow provided by Sabrina.

Chapter Seven
THE DANCE OF LIFE

"No man ever fell in love because he was good at it."
E.J.M.

In my dreams that night came a vision. I climbed a towering and majestic mountain, whose summit vanished in sun-drenched clouds. Arriving at steps of rainbow pearl, I mounted them in ascending spirals. At last I reached an azure pool, within sight of a sacred, golden shrine. I paused to rest beside the healing waters when my vision was dazzled by an awesome light, so brilliant that I shielded my gaze. There appeared within the shining rays a Being of paradisal splendor and beauty — a heavenly Goddess — majestic, powerful, sublime.

Her eyes fell upon me in a glance of measureless love. I cried out and fell upon my knees, pleading for her grace and benediction. She smiled, casting beams of gilded light in all directions. Her brilliance grew to incandescence, overpowering my mortal sight. I fell gently to earth, coming to rest in a field of flowers. Simultaneously, I awoke from my slumber.

The morning sun against my face gave rise to a primeval stirring in my heart. I stood up and walked to the edge of the forest, only steps away. I stretched my limbs and saluted the golden sun above. It was obvious why the ancient nations of Egypt and the Americas worshipped this Giver of Life. I basked in its glow, breathing in its vibrant life, gulping in the pure air charged with solar vitality. Closing my eyes, I contemplated the Divine Source within me.

I felt that the sun had become something internal. This living orb was within my soul as well as out in the cosmos. It was my own everlasting spirit, which expanded when I fed it with thoughts and noble sentiments belonging to eternity. I solemnly vowed to enlarge this inner sun through efforts springing from the love within my soul.

Sensing someone behind me, I turned to see Sabrina.

"Greetings, dear Jason," she said, smiling warmly. "May you ever walk in the light of the great sun within you, and may it illumine the way of those who cross your path." Sabrina then taught me an ancient Mayan method of attuning with the sun's energy by repeating seven times, in a prayerful attitude, the Mayan word for sun — "K'in" — pronounced, "kuh-een".

We performed the simple ritual together, then sat and ate a light breakfast of tea and Sabrina's concentrated food, which had been my diet exclusively for three days. I was feeling buoyant and energized. The strenuous exertion of our jungle adventure, combined with sweating profusely, had the effect of eliminating toxins from my body. I realized that some of the herbs given me by Chilam had accelerated the cleansing process.

"Where's Chilam?" I asked.

"He had other things to do. He told me he'd done all he could to help and that now I was stuck with you." She smiled sweetly.

"Thanks a lot," I said.

Sabrina stirred the fire with a stick. "There's far more to Chilam than meets the eye," she said.

"That's an understatement!" I responded. "He has incredible powers and abilities. Thanks to all he showed me, I'm beginning to see why I was the one to discover the medallion." I recalled my conversations with Brother Arthur, marveling at the perfection of the divine laws governing earthly life. Truly, it was useless to blame others for our circumstances.

"It was no accident," said Sabrina. "In each incarnation we pick up the threads of the old. Always there is progress, so long as we work with the tide of positive evolution."

We stamped out the remains of the fire and rapidly folded the tent. Sabrina put on her backpack and I followed her into the underbrush. We trudged through the dense forest for several hours before reaching an incline that sloped to a small stream. Crossing over, we entered a clearing. I was surprised to see a wall made of large stones. Some of them had fallen and lay strewn about, possibly as a result of earthquakes. The wall reminded me of those I had seen in Cuzco on a visit years earlier to the capital city of the ancient Inca empire in Peru. The huge stones fit together without mortar, and were so snug that a business card could not have been placed between them.

We stepped through an opening in the wall and came to a small building, half-enshrouded with large ferns and shrubs. Vines hung down and grew on the walls, creating an atmosphere of mystery. On the upper portion of the building, apparently a ruined Mayan edifice, were carvings in the stone. I recognized serpents amidst the various figures. Off to one side, about twenty yards from the building, was a massive stone carving of a human head. The impressive object measured at least six feet tall and nearly that wide, and brought to mind an Olmec stone head I had once seen in the famous archeological museum in Mexico City.

"Whew!" I exclaimed appreciatively. "Quite an enchanted place. You know all the off-the-beaten-path attractions." I smiled at Sabrina.

"The universities aren't even aware of this place yet, though I don't know how much longer it will remain that way."

"I see what you mean about America still waiting to be discovered."

Sabrina nodded, then took a step toward the trail. "Make yourself at home, Jason," she said abruptly. "I'll be back shortly."

"Where are you going?" I asked.

"For a stroll in the forest, where else?" she answered.

"To hug a tree, I suppose?"

"Good idea. Enjoy the peace." Sabrina gave a half-smile, then disappeared into the foliage.

"Enjoy your stroll," I mumbled under my breath, less than enthusiastic about seeing her depart.

I ambled around the eery jungle ruins, feeling suddenly vulnerable. As I sat upon a stone, musing, I thought I heard the sound of a soft footstep behind me. Turning abruptly, I saw nothing.

"Sabrina?" I said in a quiet voice. The jungle answered back with silence.

I stood up again and walked around the large stone head. Satisfying my curiosity and finding nothing, I turned to go back to my resting place on the fallen boulder. I stopped in my tracks. There on the stone sat a woman dressed in a traditional Mayan blouse and skirt. She looked up at me and smiled. It was Celeste.

"You again!" I exclaimed, unable to conceal my astonishment. "What are you doing here?"

"I might ask the same of you," she said softly, a slight smile on her bronzed features.

"I was here first," I said.

"Oh really? Are you certain of that?" Celeste smoothed out her white skirt, which came several inches below her knees. Her white blouse featured beautiful, red and blue embroidery, a trademark of the local Indian women.

"I'm not certain of anything," I admitted, then paused before adding, "except that you certainly have a bizarre way of entertaining yourself on long, lonely evenings in the jungle."

"I apologize for any discomfort I caused you the other night," she said in her impeccable English.

"Discomfort! I guess you should apologize. Why did you try to seduce me? I thought you were friends with Sabrina."

"Certainly we're friends. We are spiritual sisters. It was necessary that you be tested. It was my duty."

"That's some sorority you belong to. What if I had failed?"

"It isn't really a question of success or failure, but of self-knowledge. Through the experience, you learned about yourself — your loyalties and ideals — and the strength of your character in abiding by the ideals you yourself believe in. It doesn't mean your task regarding the medallion would have failed."

I thought about what she was saying, unsure what to make of her explanation.

"I guess my gain is your loss," I said. Celeste laughed loudly, revealing beautiful white teeth.

"Don't get carried away with male bravado, Jason. What makes you think I would have let you make love to me?"

"You mean, you're just a tease after all?"

"My actions were meant to serve a higher purpose. I have a beloved husband and have no desire for other involvements. As I said, it was my duty to test you."

I shrugged my shoulders. "Women!" I said softly, shaking my head.

"Celeste smiled and her eyes glistened. "The sexes must come to understand each other, treating one another with love and respect. We're all in this together."

"Loving and respecting isn't the problem," I said. "It's living with them!"

"With *them,* Jason? With each other," Celeste corrected.

"I know, I know." I waved my hand impatiently in the air.

"Do you really know? Are you sure Melissa would agree?"

"We're trying our best. Nobody ever said living with another person is easy."

"No, it's not easy. It's one of life's greatest challenges. But the reward of solving the mystery of relationship is the highest form of human joy."

"Most of us have a long way to go," I said quietly. Celeste nodded.

"Is there some secret," I volunteered, "that can illuminate relationships and make couples happy? Is that what you want to tell me? I'll be the first to admit I've made mistakes. Melissa and I sincerely love each other. Yet tensions keep creeping in which threaten our marriage."

"That's true of all couples, no matter how much love and romance they have going for them to begin with. The majority of men and women today still hold marriage as an ideal, an institution of great value, worthy of preservation. This is commendable. There are a few simple keys that the modern world needs to grasp, which, if put into practice, will dissolve countless tensions in relationships."

"Can you tell me these principles?" I asked.

"That's why I'm here," Celeste beamed. "After all, you did promise Melissa you would seek professional help, didn't you?" Celeste smiled broadly.

"You people know everything," I muttered. Celeste folded her hands and stared down at the grass for a moment, as if composing her thoughts.

"You've done some juggling in your life, haven't you, Jason?" I nodded. "That's very helpful. Juggling is marvelous for physical, mental and emotional health. But in addition, it suggests a principle of balance that may illuminate many areas of life, including relationships."

"How do you mean?"

"Picture a juggler balancing three objects in the air in front of him. What image do the juggled objects make as they move?"

"A figure eight," I said. "A lemniscate. Is that supposed to signify something special?" I knew that the lemniscate was traditionally a symbol representing infinity — it was one of the symbols engraved on the Isis Medallion — but I was not sure what it could possibly have to do with relationships.

"This image is profound," Celeste continued. It represents the act of reciprocal giving. If one of the hands, upon receiving, chose not to give, the cycle of giving and receiving, of harmony and balance, would be broken. Regarding the juggler, it means simply that his juggling comes to an end. But when you think of the juggler's two hands as being representative of two people in a close relationship such as marriage, it becomes a moral problem...in that two individuals may influence each other either for good or for ill."

"I see what you're saying. Both partners need not only to receive, allowing the partner to give; they must give in return, bringing the act of giving and receiving to completion."

"Yes, things must come full circle, then begin again. This creates a dynamic interaction. So many problems in relationships today are rooted in the fact that one of the partners does most of the giving. This produces resentment, oftentimes unconscious. In addition, it hampers the circulation of life force between a couple. Tension builds in the relationship, leading eventually to a breakdown."

"It seems so obvious when you think of it," I commented. "If one partner does most of the giving, the relationship is unbalanced, leading to inharmony."

Celeste nodded. "Eventually, things come to a head in some sort of crisis. A reciprocal giving and receiving must take place on all levels: physical, emotional and mental. This implies careful listening. Listening is far more important than most people realize. A woman especially needs to communicate feelings. If the man is inattentive, there is no reciprocity and the woman is frustrated."

"I can certainly agree with you there. It's not that I don't want to listen or communicate. It's just that I'm more interested in ideas than feelings. Or, you might say, my feelings are bound up with ideas or concepts."

Celeste smiled knowingly. "Men and women definitely tend to approach life from a different perspective," she said. "Men are more naturally taciturn. It's not easy for most of them to vocalize their feelings. With most women, it's natural and spontaneous."

"I know what you're saying. Sometimes when I try to talk about feelings, I feel so awkward. I'm always stopping to think about what I'm going to say."

"But you've grown in that direction, haven't you?" Celeste asked, a look of encouragement in her eyes.

"I hope so." I paused to reflect on the many discussions Melissa and I had shared on precisely that topic. "One thing that helped me a lot," I continued, "was just to ask simple things, such as 'what was the best part of your day?' Or, 'how did that make you feel?' Trifling as it seems, it took effort and practice for me. It seems that women tend to be much more sensitive emotionally than men, at least about most things."

Celeste nodded, a serene look in her eyes. "Men usually find it more difficult to talk openly about personal matters. A healthy reticence is valuable, but in a close partnership or marriage, there needs to be open discussion.

"Generally speaking, women solve problems more easily by conversation. Men tend naturally to brood things over in solitary silence. Either tendency carried to an extreme becomes potentially harmful. The former leads to gossip, superficiality and dependency — the latter to aloofness, isolation, and social coldness.

"When men are under stress, or feel attacked in a relationship, it's even more difficult to get them to open up emotionally. Their instinct is to wall themselves in behind a mask of tough silence. Women need to know when to let a man brood. Gradually he will come out of his shell.

"When a woman feels stressed or under attack in a relationship, she also withdraws. Her resentment often surfaces as sexual indifference and coldness. A woman needs to trust that she can express her feelings and that her partner will genuinely listen, without judgment. Trust is essential.

"Women need emotional closeness as a prerequisite to sexual intimacy. Men want sexual intimacy in order to feel emotional closeness."

There followed a long pause during which I sensed that Celeste was waiting for me to continue. "I love your image of the juggler," I said at last, "and can see how this principle of rhythmic interchange of energy is indispensable to a healthy relationship. But what about the tension created by financial pressures?" I tried to ask the question as if it were an issue for other people, not me.

Celeste's eyes took on a faraway cast. "This is a great problem for many couples in today's world," she said. "And unfortunately, there's no simple answer. It takes a great deal of patience, the willingness to make sacrifices, and the capacity for compromise. Couples have to make mutual agreements, then abide by them.

"Commitment is the cornerstone. Some think that they'll just live together and see what happens. That's preferable to plunging prematurely into an unwise marriage, but it certainly won't guarantee a successful relationship. Commitment comes first. Otherwise the relationship will lack the strength, the foundation, to withstand the difficulties which arise."

"I agree with you completely," I said. "But isn't it expecting a lot to ask people to remain together all their lives? How does a couple keep alive the flame of romance?"

Celeste smiled and her eyes twinkled. "Partners need to play together! Take walks in nature. Read the same books. Talk about a movie they've seen. Hold hands. Smile and laugh with each other. Surprise each other with love notes and gifts. Travel together. Play games or sports.

"By doing enjoyable things together, a bonding takes place in the will and in the imagination. This creates a mutual, positive karma and a common treasure of experience.

"And they must take an interest in each other as striving, growing human beings. Ideally, partners ought to participate together in activities that elevate and inspire the inner life...perhaps singing, creating artistically, or studying spiritual ideas."

"I was wondering when you'd get around to the spiritual life."

"Yes, this is the fountainhead from which all else springs. Without a shared system of values, a common spiritual substance, there's nothing in which a relationship may take root."

"Both partners have to drink from the same well," I said.

Celeste smiled. "And only the waters drawn from the depths will quench their thirst. They must share the water, yet each must cultivate a separate connection to the spirit. Then they'll both have something valuable to offer the other. Individuals must come to know themselves first. Only in that way can they create enlightened partnerships."

"I've come to believe that prayer is also indispensable," I said.

"I think you're right. Prayer has an almost magical effect, particularly if the couple prays together, as well as by themselves. The modern world must recognize that a Higher Power governs life. If a couple links up with this power, individually and together, miracles are not only possible, they become commonplace."

"I want more than anything," I said, "to be able to live a happy life and to bring happiness to my family. Is there anything else I can do to insure peace and joy in my relationship?"

"Show appreciation! Express gratitude and admiration. Convey thanks to your partner for all the good things she does and for the fine person she is. Admire all the good qualities in order to encourage and uplift her. And practice kindness. This will help you both to grow."

"I know how important this is with children. So many adults speak unkind words, or reinforce a negative self-image in children."

Celeste nodded sympathetically. "Children need to grow up in an atmosphere of warmth and harmony," she said. "The discord between parents harms the child and causes depression, listlessness or bouts of violence — depending on the child's temperament — even actual physical maladies, often not showing up until years later. Children are hypnotized and programmed by the habitual speech and attitudes of parents — especially in early childhood, for the etheric bond between parent and child has yet to be severed.

"When children are young we have the perfect opportunity to develop noble qualities in them. Tell them, while they're awake, or even during sleep — for the unconscious mind will register the impression — that they are good, loving, outstanding individuals capable of expressing marvelous qualities. In addition, the parents must try to set a good example in front of children. Of course, disagreements can't always be avoided. But if a child witnesses discord between parents, it is important that she afterwards sees the reconciliation. That way she realizes that problems are part of a process that leads eventually to harmony."

I paused reflectively, searching out my thoughts. Something was wrong. Despite the harmony and logic of our conversation — the sense and rightness of our ideas — something was absent, spoken about but not touched.

Celeste became more luminous. A ray of sunlight touched her face. She seemed almost a divinity or goddess. Bewitching. Something in her expression told me she knew my inner thoughts.

"There's something more, isn't there, Jason?"

"Yes, something more. All these explanations are true, yet ultimately words can't satisfy the heart. Do you know what I mean?"

"I do, Jason. I'm so glad for you...that is...I'm glad that you sense this, for this is the great Mystery, the Secret, the Unspeakable."

"It's the Mystery of Love, isn't it?"

Celeste nodded quietly, and the light striking her white garments shimmered beautifully, creating an otherworldly glow around her.

There was a long silence, a silence that was not empty, but filled with a sweetness that brought an indefinable joy.

Finally, I broke the stillness. "That's why people dance, I guess." Celeste's face radiated light.

"Yes, Jason. Relationship is a dance. A dance of harmony. Of perfect rhythm."

A supreme happiness filled my heart, then abruptly vanished, replaced by a piercing sadness. I had learned some of the most valuable lessons of my life. Now, ironically, I was unable to put them into practice. My heart ached as I thought of Melissa and Angelina. Would I ever see them again?

"Shall we be on our way?" came a voice from behind me. I turned to see Sabrina standing in some shadows. I spun to face her.

She quietly put on her backpack, while I took a drink from my canteen. I turned toward Celeste, but she had softly departed. I was mystified and disappointed. Sabrina started walking and I followed her.

After a long silence, I asked, "What was that building? Some kind of shrine?"

Sabrina's eyes were flashing jewels. "Yes, in a sense a shrine. It was a temple devoted to the Dance of Life."

I pondered the wisdom Celeste and I had shared, as the darkness of the jungle engulfed us.

Chapter Eight

FEAR OF FLYING

"We have to try to reveal that Light which is in us as a bud. It must blossom like a flower."
—Mother Meera

We trekked for several hours, coming to a steep hill which we climbed arduously. Thick vines hung from the trees, and these we used to help pull us up. We reached the top and paused before an abrupt chasm that fell steeply to a depth of about three hundred feet. There was no obvious way to reach the other side of the yawning precipice, nearly fifty feet away.

"What's this?" I asked. "The Grand Canyon South?"

"You might say that," Sabrina said. "It's a long way down."

"No kidding! At least there are no tourists. How do we get across?"

"You'll see," said Sabrina, "but first we need to cover some other points on our agenda."

"Agenda?"

"Certainly, Jason. Don't tell me you're not aware by now that there's a pattern in your experiences."

"You mean, 'a method to the madness'?"

"If you prefer." Sabrina removed her backpack and sat on a small rock.

"Tell me how you feel?" she asked. "I mean physically."

"Well, my legs are sure sore."

"And?"

"And I feel strong, healthy...almost cleansed."

"Good. Anything else?"

I paused a minute, thinking. "I feel light...I guess you could say."

"Perfect," said Sabrina, smiling.

"I'm glad to know I got the right answer."

"You hit it on the button. As you know, 'light' has a double meaning. 'Light' is illumination, and 'light' is absence of weight. These are the states of being to which we aspire."

"I guess that's why they call it enlightenment," I said.

Sabrina stood up abruptly and I did the same. "All your experiences, thus far, Jason, should have confirmed within your awareness that you are more than just your physical form."

"I'm very aware of that. I know that my real, intrinsic being is not my physical body. My body's the carriage in which I ride."

"Exactly. The goal is for you to eventually perceive the higher or more subtle energy bodies, those which interpenetrate the physical, giving life and animation to your dense form."

"My spirit bodies," I said.

Sabrina nodded. "There are many levels, or densities, within our multi-dimensional being. Those closest to the physical are called, in our school, the vital or etheric, and the astral, or emotional. Out of these emerge the so-called mental body. The still higher bodies — the translucent receptacles of the Divine Spark — need not concern you for the moment, for your work is primarily upon these sheaths.

"Now look at me carefully," she commanded. "Not at my form, but around it. What do you see?" I stared at Sabrina, focusing on the area several inches from her body. At first I saw nothing. Then she gently touched my elbow.

Immediately, I saw a bluish glow around her, in which gradually other colors became apparent.

"Amazing!" I said. "I'm seeing your aura."

"You are seeing the denser levels of my total energy body, forming the auric field. These emanations are formed of my vital energy, my thoughts and feelings. In time you will be able to sustain this subtle vision, or clairvoyance, which I'm now assisting you in perceiving. But this must not be done by mechanical or artificial means."

"You mean, no substance abuse?"

"No abuse of anything. Maintain physical and mental health. Avoid fanaticism and extremism. Let moderation be the key. It is not by externals, but by the quality of one's inner life that progress is made. The methods used in this school of initiation are exclusively those of consciousness."

"Methods of consciousness? I'm not sure if I follow you."

"In other words, by subtle alterations in your habitual states of thought and feeling, combined with the transformation of your will, you will eventually reach the loftiest spiritual plateaus."

"Arthur and I talked about these things. It certainly doesn't sound difficult."

"It's simple, but not easy."

"Can we get more specific?" I asked.

"Give me the medallion," Sabrina commanded. I took off the jewelled goddess and handed it to her. "If one could decipher the symbolism on this artifact," she said, "he would have a complete path of higher development outlined for him. The medallion contains specific instructions and exact teachings, hidden in its emblematic language, by which one may ascend to Godhood and conscious immortality. Words alone are not enough. One must embrace Sophia, the divine wisdom. To the initiated, these glyphs spell out the Way. In addition, the medallion is a talisman, a magical transformer."

Sabrina took me by the shoulders and spun me around, facing the sun. She held the relic in her hand. "Hold your head upright," she said, "eyes open, but avoid looking directly at the sun." She began to recite an incantation in a bizarre tongue, then she traced an unknown symbol on my forehead. Pausing in her chant for a moment, Sabrina spoke loudly.

"Jason, behold!"

Instantly, there was a dazzling flash of illumination, and the entire world became a universe of light. I fell to my knees in astonishment. Everything seemed to pulse from the inside with its own radiance. I saw that all material forms — all animals, plants and trees, mine and Sabrina's physical bodies — even the stones and the earth itself, were essentially composed of light. The sun, the stars and planets were resplendent spheres of spiritual luminosity. That which we saw with our naked eye was the densest, most physical layer of the actual planet or star. Behind the physical universe throbbed a spiritual universe of astounding beauty — a world of living light.

The physical world dissolved into a breathtaking, radiant kaleidoscope — spectral and symphonic. The whirl of electrons, the harmonic blend of particles and waves, formed a living Dance. Transparent colors, fantastic hues, weaved together in a majestic, living array. All was alive, glowing, perfect — crowned with Excellence. All entities, all emanations of all worlds, were poised in delicate, perfect balance. And the many strands of color, tone, and light were infused with a transcendent emotion — heavenly Joy.

I saw that every being was interconnected by billions of light threads flowing from an unknown center, above and beyond the Vision. Life was a shimmering, intricate web of subtle interweavings — a tapestry of luminous gossamer. All life forms shared a common, benign origin. I sensed a spectacular mystery, vast and incomprehensible. The entire creation was the garment of some nameless, glorious Being — Self-contained, containing all, gigantic. An endless, compassionate Life, resounding with Bliss, radiant with Love.

I saw the energy vortices, or chakras — what Chilam referred to as the "flowers of the soul" — which energized my spiritual bodies. Intricate streams of delicate light-rays spun out from these wheels or chakras, which indeed resembled the open petals of a flower.

Billions of tiny light flecks danced in this rarefied spiritual atmosphere. I knew that every living thing upon earth, even the minutest plant or animal form, was animated by a light spark such as these.

Sabrina touched my forehead once again and I regained my normal perception of the physical world. For several minutes neither of us spoke, respecting the grandeur of the vision I was allowed to behold. I was overcome with wonder at the majesty within and behind the natural world — of which physical nature was an expression.

Sabrina broke the silence. "You carry within yourself at all times, Jason, the most exalted states of consciousness. You have also at all times the means of achieving this awareness."

"I'm overwhelmed, Sabrina. The universe we live in is miraculous beyond description. I've always believed that, while on earth, we live simultaneously in a spiritual universe. Now I've seen that it's true."

Sabrina had more to show me. She smoothed some dirt with her hands, then with her finger sketched a six-petalled flower, identical to the flower at the center of the medallion.

"The Flower of Life," I said.

Sabrina smiled, gesturing toward the emblem. "The Flower of Life also reveals the way to clairvoyance or seership. In other words...the means by which one effects the metamorphosis."

"How is that?" I asked.

"Each petal of the flower represents an activity of consciousness which elevates the soul and awakens the inner spiritual organs, or chakras." She pointed with her finger at each petal in turn.

"They are as follows: The first is positivity. All your thoughts and emotions must become positive. You must be able to see the good element in everything. Always there is something beautiful to be found. When negativity is transcended, your world is transformed, becoming lovely, joyous...almost heavenly. Seek ever the good, the beautiful and the true.

"Second comes concentration, or control of thought. Our thoughts must not occur in a random, haphazard manner. We must guide the flow of our thinking and thus also our feelings. We must master our minds, subduing elements which arise without our permission, so to speak, thereby training our powers of thought.

"Third," she said, indicating yet another petal on the flower, "is control of action, or the guidance of our will. We must develop strength, tenacity and endurance in our will-life. When we make a resolve, we must carry it through without fail, so long as it is an honorable, worthy intention. Be not a leaf in the wind. Obey your own inner commands. Always remember, repetition of specific actions strengthens the will.

"Fourth, the student of higher wisdom develops inner tranquility. This is serenity of spirit, or equanimity in the life of feelings. Nothing must for long throw you off balance or shatter your poise. This is the true meaning of the modern expression, 'going with the flow'. Our inner activity produces emotional calm and inner peace, which in turn produces strength of mind and stability of character. The keynote of the inner life becomes gentleness.

"Fifth, be open-minded and tolerant of other viewpoints. This means careful, attentive listening and the withholding of snap judgments. You must be willing to listen to any and learn from all, even the most humble. This attitude of open-mindedness does wonders to expand and illumine the inner life, stimulating the growth of the light in the soul.

"Sixth," she said, her finger touching the final point, "you must develop a profound gratitude for life and the gifts and opportunities which each moment brings. Life itself is a gift made possible by the deeds of innumerable beings. The natural kingdoms provide us with a bounty of beauty. The earth and the heavens are a vast treasurehouse. One's heart should beat in thankfulness to the All of Life. This state of constant gratitude exalts the soul, creating happiness, and lifts one into the celestial regions.

"Last, all these activities must be integrated and practiced together, without undue exertion on our part. Of course, this takes time. And they must be linked together by one essential, unifying virtue, which may be visualized as a pink rose in the center of your heart — the practice of loving-kindness.

"When kindness characterizes your approach to life, and when the qualities I've mentioned become second nature, so that they are done almost without effort, a striking metamorphosis will take place in the soul.

"The petals of the subtle, spiritual organs, or chakras, become pliant and alive, and begin gently to revolve. Inner perception, both seeing and hearing, quietly unfolds. You are born onto the higher planes of life, possessing direct vision of the heavenly spheres. Angels rejoice, for the world gains a conscious seer, a clairvoyant, an Initiate of Life.

"This, Jason, is the way and the goal. It is a path of inner and outer freedom. Your inner life becomes one of quiet attention and heavenly contemplation. Your outer activity becomes a source of helpfulness and blessing to all. Thus you kindle the fires of your spirit and illumine the inner regions of the soul. You will then radiate strength and light, becoming a beacon in the darkness of the world."

Sabrina's words were inspiring. "It seems to me," I said, "that what you're describing is more elevated than what people today call 'channeling,' or trance mediumship."

Sabrina smiled. "Each of us is created to be a vessel," she explained, "or channel, for our divine spirit or Higher Self. But I'm glad you realize that the goal of spiritual endeavor is not to become an unconscious trance channel, wherein a disembodied entity takes over your physical and etheric organisms.

"The aim of true spiritual training is to develop the organs of the soul...the chakras...by the practice of virtue, and gradually awaken a conscious perception of the higher dimensions. You may then, in full awareness, contact the exalted beings and converse with them as you would with an esteemed friend on the physical plane of reality. This way we become co-creators with the heavenly worlds. The ideal is that the spiritual aspirant remain fully conscious. This is the path of the Higher Mysteries."

I paused admiringly, then shook my head. "Sometimes the goal seems such a long way off. I feel as if I've hardly gotten off the ground."

"A knowledge of the path is important. But don't get discouraged by constantly measuring yourself against the ideal. Develop your ideas each day. Cultivate the belief that your thoughts will lead you deeper into the truth...that they have the power to transform you.

"No individual is ever a finished product. When you're ripe...you start to rot. Stay green and growing."

I marveled at Sabrina's description of the inner path. A vivid light shone from her eyes, and for a moment I had to look away. She gave me precious little time to contemplate that day's revelations.

"Now, Jason," she said after a short pause, "let's put knowledge into practice. You know theoretically that you are a light being. It's time to realize it with every cell of your body."

Sabrina gave me the medallion, picked up her backpack, and walked several steps away from the edge of the chasm's gaping jaws. I watched her nervously as she took several deep breaths. She closed her eyes, apparently concentrating deeply, harnessing her forces.

"Follow me!" she shouted, then raced toward the rim and leaped!

I gasped, disbelieving. Sabrina catapulted herself aloft, and for an instant she appeared to hover in the air above the dreadful cleft. Her body soared in a graceful arc and she landed gently on the other side.

My mouth dropped open in sheer amazement. "How in the world did you do that?" My voice was almost a whisper, but she could hear me clearly.

Sabrina took off her backpack and ran her fingers through her hair. "Believe me, it's not at all difficult. This is child's play. Now it's your turn."

"No way!" I insisted. "I'm not that crazy. I may have been born in the afternoon, but not yesterday afternoon!"

"Jason, you must first believe it's possible. The spirit within you is more powerful even than gravity. This is not a test of athletic ability. It's a test of faith."

"Oh great," I said, sarcasm in my voice. "I guess you call this one 'the leap of faith.' Literally!"

"Shall I take your hand, little one?" Sabrina asked gently, the slightest trace of condescension in her voice. Her chiding manner, though nearly imperceptible, both irritated and motivated me.

"You now know beyond doubt, Jason, that it can be done. You must believe that you can do it. Have no fear. I will help you."

I stood up and walked several steps away from the rim, as Sabrina had done. She had a gentle smile on her face, visible across the distance which separated us. I hesitated, my heart pounding.

"You're absolutely certain I can do it?" I asked her.

"Positive! Look at my eyes. What do you see?" As I stared at her, a thin line of golden light — stretching from my eyes to hers — gradually became distinct. "Do you see it?" she asked.

"Yes, a strand of light."

"It's a bridge...a bridge of light. When you leap, know unshakably in your heart that you will span that bridge. Have faith, my friend. Never doubt that I'll assist you." She smiled, and from across the precipice I felt a stream of loving energy flow from her to me, uniting us. The love she projected made me feel buoyant.

I shook my hands loosely at my side, breathed deeply, and stared beyond the canyon's edge.

"Yes!" I shouted, and raced towards the chasm. I leaped above the abyss, never taking my eyes off the golden thread. Gravity seemed suspended and I flew, landing gently at Sabrina's feet.

"Remember, Jason," she said, smiling and offering me her hand. "Love weighs nothing."

Chapter Nine

PATHS TO THE FUTURE

"The greatest treasures one may find,
Are truths eternal of the mind." E.J.M.

We slept that night in Sabrina's tent, continuing our journey with the first rays of the dawn. We fell into a rhythm of peaceful contemplation, speaking rarely. This gave me time to wonder at this new world into which I had stumbled — a world where the miraculous was commonplace. I was awestruck at the powers latent within the Spirit Self of each person.

Sabrina had told me that silence was a balm to the soul, and that too much talk was destructive to the physical organism as well as to the subtle energy bodies. She said that the speech of the majority of human beings was almost entirely trivial and insignificant. This had the effect of building a barrier between the conscious mind and one's higher nature, thus blunting the sense for the eternal truths. She said that the future would bring gigantic changes in the manner in which we viewed speech, for the spoken word held the secret of divine creation. "When a god speaks," she told me, "universes come into being."

Soon after mid-day, we paused beside a bubbling stream to fill our canteens. Sabrina gestured toward a brightly colored bird, similar to a toucan. I was amazed at the enormous variety of jungle wildlife.

"What's on your mind?" she asked, breaking our silence.

"I'm speechless," I said, grinning.

"Good. We're making progress."

"Actually," I continued, "I was thinking about the world predicament. Perhaps I'm just naturally morbid."

"You're just sensitive, and have an awakened sense of responsibility."

"Sometimes I question," I persisted, "if we're really making progress. That is...as a civilization. In many ways things seem to be getting worse."

Sabrina started off again and I followed a step behind. "This historical moment is unusual," she explained. "Many are part of an ascending spiral, working to create a better world. Others have become enmeshed in the cultural degeneracy of the age that is dying. This is tragic, but in the larger picture, those who slip backwards will have opportunities for development at a later date.

"The struggle today is not really east versus west, or capitalism fighting communism, nor is it primarily one spiritual ideology against another. It's those who seek to dominate, exploit, and control against those who wish to liberate the human spirit...the forces of enslavement against the forces of individual and spiritual sovereignty."

We paused for a moment to lift a fallen tree from our path. "I can see," I said, "why it's necessary to be a strong individual. We can't be free if we're weak. We need to think and act on our own initiative."

"Exactly," agreed Sabrina. "We can't have power if we have no self-determination. The individuality of the human being is sacred."

"You know, it occurs to me," I added, "that tyrants and totalitarians must love any philosophy that tells people to passively accept whatever happens to them. That makes us pawns in the hands of the elite controllers."

"I can tell that you're thinking of the Trilateralists again." Sabrina smiled knowingly. "And you're right. People need to be strong to resist the hidden plans of the most diabolic faction within the elitist groups. If people truly understood the aims of the elites, they would be shocked beyond belief."

"You mean," I said, "their plans for a One World totalitarian state?"

"Yes," said Sabrina. "Few realize the lengths to which the powermongers are prepared to go to insure complete global dominance." Sabrina's tone was serious — more so than usual.

"I thought I knew a lot already. Is there more?"

Sabrina nodded grimly. "Something so sinister as to be almost beyond belief — what the Biblical book of Revelation calls 'the mark of the beast.'"

"How do you mean?"

Sabrina sighed and paused. We had reached a slight clearing in the dense foliage and she sat down on a lichen-covered rock. I sat across from her, happy to have a few minutes' rest.

"I think you realize," she explained, "that the goal of the financial insiders is to eliminate cash."

"I'm aware of that," I responded, mentioning my experience in the San Francisco branch of the Federal Reserve Bank.

"Of course," Sabrina continued, "the interim step may be to issue new currency — possibly even a single global currency. But this would only be a stepping stone to switching entirely to the use of debit cards — what people call credit cards."

"They want to obliterate the underground economy and control all financial transactions," I said.

"That's only part of it," Sabrina continued. "These credit cards would make use of the most sophisticated new computer technology. On each of these cards would be placed a microchip with complete records of each individual, kept from cradle to grave. It would be a detailed file, making possible close government scrutiny and control of our private lives. "

"It really is diabolic."

"But that's not all," Sabrina continued. "That's just the preliminary step. Once everyone has been rounded up into the network of financial and information control made possible by mandatory use of these cards, the elites would lower the boom."

"Lower the boom?"

Sabrina paused, searching me with her deep brown eyes. "The next step, Jason, would be to imbed the chip beneath the skin of every person."

"Beneath the skin! Are you joking? They must think we're sheep!"

"Serfs, Jason — mere serfs. No financial transactions would be possible without use of the chip, which would most likely be placed in the wrist — although some would even like it to be in the forehead. Those who refused to participate in this system would be rogues — outcasts — unable to exist within establishment society."

"How horrible!" I shuddered.

"But wait; there's more," Sabrina continued, her eyes gleaming with an opalescent light.

"What else could there be?" I protested.

"Within each chip would be injected a living micro-organism — a type of virus. This virus could be activated by remote control. If someone outlived his usefulness — or if he tried to escape into the wilderness — the social manipulators would have only to electronically trigger the chip to release the virus into the victim's bloodstream, killing him."

I shook my head in disbelief, reaching impulsively for my canteen. "It's too awful to contemplate," I said after swallowing. "Can these monsters be stopped?"

"They must be stopped," Sabrina answered. "Which is why it's critical that people be independent and have minds of their own, resistant to media brainwashing. The controllers would like us to be submissive — a docile planetary flock. Strong individuals working in concert with one another can defeat the dark plans of these misguided souls.

"What's needed is a return to sacred living — enough good and spirited people living to benefit not only themselves, but the world."

We got up from the rock and left the small clearing, continuing our trek through the dense forest. After an interlude of quiet reflection, I once more broke the silence.

"It seems to me," I said, pushing aside a branch that blocked our way, "that in modern western societies, at least in the U.S., the individual is becoming less important. Even in many of the new spiritual philosophies, the 'ego' is considered only in a negative light. But if we suppress or deny our egos, don't we, at the same time, weaken our individuality?"

"You bring up a very important issue," Sabrina answered, "around which there is considerable cloudy thinking, particularly in spiritual circles. Much of it arises from a confusion of terms.

"Many people become weak in themselves — thereby susceptible to manipulation or control — because they mistakenly believe they should somehow dissolve their 'I,' or intrinsic self. Rather than use the term 'ego,' it would be better if psychology employed the term 'not-self,' or 'false self,' to refer to that element of our personality which is motivated entirely by selfishness, and needs therefore to be transformed.

"Our modern use of the word 'ego' comes largely from the nineteenth-century depth psychology of Freud. However, Freud used the word 'ich' in his writings, German for the pronoun 'I.' For some reason the English translators of Freud picked the Latin word 'ego.' When a citizen of ancient Rome said 'ego' he meant 'I,' but today many people use it to refer to an unreal, impermanent, or inferior part of ourselves. Thus, I prefer the term 'not-self,' for the 'I' is an expression of our true and eternal being."

We paused a moment at the crest of a hill to catch our breath. "So there's a big difference," I said, "between our 'I' and what you call the 'not-self.'"

"That's correct. The 'I' is the kernel of our spirit...the seed of the immortal, I AM PRESENCE. The false self or 'not-self,' what many people call the 'ego,' is the petty, immature image — or projection — of ourselves which masquerades as our real 'I.'" Sabrina pointed to a vivid green snake curled up in the elbow of a tree. So absorbed was I in the conversation that I didn't think to ask if it were venomous.

"I see what you mean," I said. "If we destroyed our 'I,' we would be eliminating our individuality — the essence of who we are. Without an 'I', there could be no 'I AM.'"

"Precisely," Sabrina responded. "The 'I' is the point of pure self-awareness at the center of our identity — the core of our individuality. It's because men and women have an 'I,' or individualized spirit, that we are able to stand with an upright posture, unlike the animals." A noise above our heads caused us to look up. In a nearby tree we observed a monkey chattering at us from the safety of a high branch.

"Our vertical posture," continued Sabrina, "represents a totally different orientation to the world, a unique consciousness. The 'I' makes possible human freedom...the independence of the mind, the emancipation of the soul, and the liberation of the spirit."

We drank from our canteens before continuing. "The Higher Self, or Divine Spirit," she went on, "never fully incarnates. Much of it remains in its complete glory upon the celestial planes. But in the process of incarnation, a fragment of the Spirit Self descends into our personality. It is our psychological center, our individuality; it is our 'I.'"

"But we're not supposed to become egoistic or self-centered," I said, brushing away a mosquito brazen enough to ignore my herbal insect repellant. "I can imagine people misinterpreting what you mean."

"Not if we carefully distinguish between the 'I' and the false self.

"Egotism, that is, excessive self-love, must certainly be overcome. Humility is necessary in order to grow spiritually. But without an 'I,' the personality would have no autonomous center, becoming vulnerable to external controls.

"At mankind's present stage of development, individuals experience the 'I' as a dynamic center of self-will and self-awareness within the feeling life, or soul. So long as the 'I' lives only for itself, it will never know happiness. When it begins to seek God, or the Divine — and benefits others as an expression of this seeking — it begins to find enduring contentment.

"Gradually, the 'I,' as a separate energy of consciousness, unites with the Spirit Self. This entails a gigantic transformation in one's feelings and awareness. But as this century's leading psychologist, Carl Jung, realized, the 'I' is not something negative to be dissolved or overcome. Without an individualized spirit, each of us would be a slave following the dictates of others."

"My understanding," I said, "is that self-development is really a matter of metamorphosis, in the manner of the butterfly emerging from its cocoon. We ascend from a limited, selfish consciousness to universal, divine awareness. But we never lose our individuality. To do so would spoil the fruits of evolution."

"I like your image," said Sabrina. "Spiritual growth involves the purification of the self, not its elimination. This is done by introducing a divine element — the Higher Self — into our souls through prayer, meditation, spiritual study, and helping others. This is the great work of human ennoblement, leading to the transfiguration of the personality — what the Medieval alchemists referred to metaphorically as the process of changing base metal into gold."

She then taught me the Mayan expression, "In Lak'ech Yelir," meaning "I am another yourself." She explained that two mature individuals need not compete, but can live with respect for each other's uniqueness, while recognizing their inner unity.

"As the race matures," she continued, "people will develop a strong sense of community. Spiritual advancement implies a sense of responsibility for the good of all. That choice must not arise from imposed legislation, but from a moral perception arising from the free human spirit.

"The healthy social life is born when the virtues of each person are expressed in the community, and when the community's welfare is reflected in the deeds of each soul. In the future, individual liberty will go hand in hand with community awareness."

"I couldn't have said it better myself," I said teasingly, appreciative of Sabrina's explanation of these ideas, which I had been wrestling with for some time.

Sabrina continued walking and I followed a half-step behind. "With all the darkness on the planet now," I persisted, "how can you be certain the future world will be a better one?"

Sabrina replied with complete confidence. "The Guiding Ones have decreed that this be so. Ideally the new, enlightened culture will emerge as a result of the thoughts and actions of enough inspired people — people who can resist the enslavers through positive methods. It's wise to be aware of the manipulations of the dark ones, but our work is with the constructive, beneficial forces. We must overcome evil with the practice of goodness, staying joyous and inspired at all times, dwelling always in the light.

"However, if too few people awaken in time, the positive powers do have a contingency plan."

"A contingency plan?"

Sabrina hesitated an instant. "Yes," she continued. "Mother Nature herself will convulse, wrecking the tyrannical plans of the elites."

"I suppose that would pretty much spoil everyone else's picnic at the same time," I said, considering the implications of Sabrina's statement.

"Sadly, I'm afraid you're right. For that reason alone it would be far better if the good people of planet earth join

together to put an end to the destruction of the earth's natural
resources, learning to live in harmony with nature and one
another. If not, the earth itself is more than capable of bringing
the existing economic and political order to its knees."

Before I could press Sabrina further on the subject of earth
upheavals, she expanded her vision of the future. "Regardless
of the means," she said, "in a few years there will emerge an
enlightened global culture, despite current appearances to the
contrary. All societies will contribute their particular genius,
and every culture will be respected. The age to come, following
on the heels of the coming tribulations, will unite the best of
all lands and people. Human beings will take enormous strides
in their journey toward mastery, developing powers and abilities
that would today be considered miraculous."

I smiled at Sabrina's words. "So we'll develop paranormal
abilities. I have to admit that I'm fascinated by the idea of
vanishing, walking on water, communicating telepathically,
levitating objects...all the things I've read about for years in
the spiritual books, and which were theoretical until I met you
and Arthur. Will large numbers of people really be able to do
all these things?"

"The great majority will. Such abilities are a natural expression of the unfolding spiritual faculties. Within the next
fifty years the talents you mention will start to become commonplace, and will be invaluable in building the new civilization. But they won't be used for show or mere personal
satisfaction. We're not talking about a race of Marvel comic
book characters; these mental and soul powers — what in the
east are called 'siddhis' — are inherent in the developed human
spirit. After the present generation has been humbled by coming
events, the new race, chastened and ennobled, will unfold
faculties of mind that will dazzle and astonish. Yes, it's something to anticipate with joy. In the meantime, you can best
prepare for the awakening of these transcendent gifts by prac-
ticing living happily each day, in loving service to all of life."

I reflected on Sabrina's prophetic glimpses. "The development of telepathy alone," I said, "would drastically change our whole social, economic and political life. All the criminal types, and the elites who want to control us, would be unable to manipulate or coerce for personal advantage. Their thoughts and motives would be visible to all, like an open book. Now that's something to look forward to!" I said emphatically.

"Very true. But it's a two-edged sword. Telepathy implies great moral sensitivity to the feelings of others. Ugly secrets can't be hidden. Our innermost thoughts and feelings are exposed to strangers as well as loved ones. The human race will need to take a huge stride forward in kindness, love, compassion and understanding. People will become honest of necessity. Our thoughts will be heard, our motives seen. Humans will finally live in peace."

"It will be a beautiful world," I said, inspired by a surge of happiness.

"Yes," agreed Sabrina. "The desire to dominate and exploit the earth will come to an end, at least for the coming cycle. This is the goal of the spiritual brotherhoods, for which they have prepared many millennia."

"Are these the Mystery Schools Arthur told me about?" Sabrina nodded. We were quiet for several minutes, engaged in our own reflections.

"Why don't the spiritual brotherhoods intervene to put an end to the wicked goals of the power elites?" I asked, breaking the silence.

"To do so," answered Sabrina, "would break spiritual law. The beneficent powers always leave individuals free, permitting us to learn by our errors, developing our spirit selves in freedom."

I thought about our conversation — and wrestled with conflicting emotions — as we struggled up the steep path. I was deeply disturbed by the plans of the elites, yet simultaneously inspired by Sabrina's vision of an enlightened future, beyond the current global crisis.

"Remember, Jason," said Sabrina, interrupting my pondering, "now more than ever the world needs our light — all the brilliance our souls can muster. Don't let world conditions depress you. When you think of problems, or places of global crisis, bathe them with a healing light. A helpful practice is to visualize a golden star or radiant sun above you — expressive of your spirit self — and project beams of light from this luminous source, illuminating the troubled area."

We reached the crest of another high ridge and gazed in admiration at the emerald sea below us.

"Isn't it beautiful!" Sabrina exclaimed.

"Like paradise," I said, wiping the sweat from my brow. "But then there's the humidity." For a moment I thought I saw an object flash far below in the dense green, then dismissed it as a play of light or trick of my mind.

We began our descent from the ridge on a path that went beside a waterfall and crossed several streams. To my surprise, the downward climb took much longer than I expected, and I realized we were entering a valley. The valley was positioned in such a way, sandwiched between tall ridges, that I'd been unaware of it.

We walked about a half mile until a cluster of giant boulders blocked any further advance. To my surprise, Sabrina jumped onto one of the rocks and, climbing rapidly, was soon almost forty feet above me, having followed a series of steps that were not discernible from my angle. Then, abruptly, she vanished into the rock.

"Not again!" I said under my breath. I stared in bewilderment, wondering what I was supposed to do. I was unable to scale the tall, smooth boulders.

"You aren't giving up now, are you?" came a voice. I looked up and saw Sabrina perched on an overhang, smiling mischievously. "Over there," she said, pointing to a spot where I might place my foot. She began to indicate cleverly camouflaged foot- and hand-holds, hewn into the rock, by which I was able to scale the pile of stones. Minutes later, I stood beside her on a huge slab.

"Ingenious," I remarked. "But where did you go? You seemed to disappear."

"I went here," she said, pointing to what I thought was solid stone. Looking closely, I saw there was a narrow gap between the rocks, between which we could pass. We followed a kind of tight canyon, or corridor, that weaved between the high boulders, and within minutes were on the other side of the seemingly impassable stones.

To my astonishment, directly in front of us, not more than two hundred yards away, stood a small step pyramid, constructed in the Mayan fashion out of large stone blocks. We descended from the boulders, crossed a stretch of green, and walked around the pyramid. What I saw took my breath away. There, on the other side, was the stuff of myth and legend brought to life.

We stood at the entrance to a hidden valley. Several waterfalls cascaded from tall cliffs high above, joining into a glistening stream that meandered through the valley floor. A green carpet of luxurious grass covered the earth. It was a veritable Shangri-la.

The valley was narrow, probably not more than half a mile across, and appeared to stretch little more than a mile or so. The vegetation was incredibly lush, and a breeze blew briskly, providing relief from the heat and humidity.

Colorful gardens and fruit orchards covered much of the valley floor. Lovely homes made of stone, earth and wood dotted the landscape. The whole vista was dominated by a second pyramid, of much greater size than the first, and a majestic, white-pillared temple, resembling those of ancient Greece. There were people going about their work, many dressed in white, loose-fitting garments, others looking much like the Mayan descendants of today. A group of children played happily, and their sweet voices struck my ears like charmed music.

I walked behind Sabrina, coming at last to the foot of the large pyramid, a monumental architectural wonder. I gazed upward admiringly.

"Welcome, Jason," came a deep voice from behind me. Astonished, I turned to see who knew my name.

There stood three impressive figures, clad in long, flowing garments of white, embroidered with purple and gold. Standing in the center was a tall, fair-skinned man, with blonde hair falling nearly to his shoulders. Beside him on his right stood Chilam, the old shaman, holding in one hand the red flower I had left him three days before, looking as fresh as the moment I plucked it. He held in his other hand the cherished photograph of my family.

To the left of the tall man in priestly garments was Celeste, the jungle enchantress.

I had reached my destination.

Chapter Ten

THE HIDDEN VALLEY

"Love is eternal; those who love never die." E.J.M.

1 stared in amazement at the trinity of people before me, realizing that I had entered one of the fabled Lost Cities.

"Greetings, little brother," said the tall, fair-skinned man in the priestly robe. His face radiated peace; his bearing suggested authority. He cast a luminous glance upon me and I felt instantly serene.

"With deepest pleasure," said the priest, "we welcome you to our modest home, unknown to but a few in the outer world. Here in the valley, I'm called Brother Peter." We shook hands, and the sweetest happiness filled my heart. His touch conveyed a charge of energy and I felt vitalized in his presence. I sensed I was in the aura of a great Initiate.

Brother Peter acknowledged his companions on either side. "I believe you have already met my two colleagues," he said, "Brother Chilam and Sister Celeste." Each of them bowed to me slightly, smiling warmly, and I returned the gesture. They looked startlingly different dressed in the white garments of the Brotherhood.

Chilam handed me the photograph. "The only things you keep are those you give away," he said. "You offered it to life, and life has returned it."

Celeste, especially, was striking, not only in her bronze beauty, but also in her manner, which seemed so dignified, so noble. She reached out her hand and I clasped it warmly.

"I must tell Sabrina what a bright pupil you are," she said, smiling sincerely.

"Thanks for providing such stimulating lesson material," I responded.

We began to walk around the large pyramid, a gigantic jewel in a setting of verdant green. "There can be no growth of soul and spirit without resistance," said Peter, walking beside me. He spoke with conviction, yet his manner was peaceful — almost humble. "Because of the resistance provided by material substance, the physical dimensions of reality provide the ideal classroom for the spirit to demonstrate self-mastery. In that way we come to know ourselves as divine, immortal, and perfect.

"You have accomplished a difficult task in bringing the relic of Isis to our retreat. Please accept our heartfelt gratitude and congratulations. We call our home Poseid in memory of the lost Atlantean Isle of that name, upon which, many thousands of years ago, our mystic order was founded. We are known as the Brotherhood of the Star."

"I'm honored beyond words to be here," I said. "I feel completely undeserving." To my surprise, all four of them laughed. It occurred to me that these remarkable people, all obviously learned in the deeper secrets of life, were neither solemn nor artificially pious.

"You have no need to feel that way," Sabrina said, "You have earned the right to visit the Lost City. Didn't I tell you there was a way to enter?"

"Of course," I replied, "It's just a matter of having the right connections."

Peter had a sublime expression on his face. "You needn't have friends in high places," he said. "When one is ready, nothing can bar him entrance into one of our retreats. Until that time, nothing he may attempt will lead to success; our Brotherhood may not be stormed by force. The key to entry is the condition of one's soul. Until sufficient progress is made, the unsuited will be repelled from our hidden sanctuary as if by an invisible power."

We paused at one corner of the pyramid and I gazed toward the apex, marveling at the immense monument. Both pyramids in Poseid were built of enormous individual stones, fitting together with exact precision. The smaller pyramid had nine levels going up to the top, in the style of some of the Mayan temples. The largest had smooth sides, in the manner of the Egyptian pyramids when originally constructed. Both monuments had steps going up the center of the four inclines. An extraordinary feature of each was that they were smooth as glass, as if their sides had been polished by jewelers.

"How is it," I asked, "that the pyramids here are so smoothly finished? That must have required the labor of an enormous number of people."

"Not at all, my friend," said Peter. "These pyramids, as also the great ones of Egypt and ancient Atlantis, were not built with teams of slaves, as your academics presume. The pyramids were constructed using mental powers, and an application of natural forces which your science has not yet developed. The stones were cut using light technology, a variation on what today is called the laser. The massive blocks, weighing several tons, were raised by levitation and sound, a process which neutralized the gravitational field.

"Once the stones were in place, it was merely a matter of removing the excess mass from them. All the substance that did not conform to the precise desired dimension was dematerialized through a combination of exact visualization and energized will. It's no exaggeration to say that their dimension and proportion were not cut by hand or by tool, but rather by mind. In this way the ancients were able to accomplish feats on a scale and magnitude incomprehensible to modern engineering, unschooled in the science of the initiates."

"It's so awesome," I said.

"In the very near future," said Sabrina, "your civilization, once it has been karmically chastised, will unfold these powers and will rival the ancient world in the rediscovered technology of the mind. The architecture and construction of the future will be based upon spiritual science."

After circumambulating the enormous pyramid, Brother Peter placed his hand on my shoulder. "Please excuse me for the moment," he said. "I have a few matters to attend to. I look forward to seeing you this evening, Jason...at the ceremony. Until then, your friends here will be most happy to give you a tour of our jungle home." With a slight, dignified bow, Peter walked away from our group.

We watched Brother Peter depart in the direction of the Grecian-style temple. I could see that Sabrina, Chilam and Celeste held him in the highest regard.

"What ceremony did he mean?" I asked.

"The ceremony for the purification of the medallion," answered Sabrina.

"Purification?" I asked. "Was my influence that bad?" The three of them chuckled and shook their heads.

"As you can imagine," said Celeste, "after many centuries of contact with the coarse vibrations of humanity, and after being subjected to dark forms of magic, many negative influences have become attached to the relic. By a process of cleans-

ing, the vibration of this relic — in its function as a talisman
— will be restored to its original pristine state before it is to
be presented to the Lady of the Medallion."

"The Lady of the Medallion?" I asked, wondering to myself
if that might be the heavenly lady whose presence I had felt
while wearing the ancient relic.

Sabrina smiled. "Be patient, Jason. You'll soon understand."

We began to ascend the pyramid steps. The point of the
capstone, composed of green marble, stood more than two
hundred feet above the jungle floor. Chilam told me that the
monument was constructed as a smaller replica of the great
Pyramid of Gizeh.

After several minutes we reached the top-most step, just
beneath the capstone. Sabrina remarked that under normal
circumstances the capstone would be of an imperishable alloy
of brass, copper and gold — or at least plated gold — but
green marble was chosen in this instance so as not to create a
reflection that might be visible from the air. The steps led into
a chamber just beneath the capstone, but we remained outside,
gazing across the valley.

"My understanding," I said, "is that the true function of
the pyramid in ancient times was as a temple of initiation. Isn't
that so?"

"Yes," said Sabrina, "that was its primary function, although
it had many others — as a school, as a focus of meditation,
and as a repository of cosmic knowledge. The pyramid form
is itself an expression of divine geometry — conveying knowledge to the wise — a letter in the cosmic alphabet of the gods.

"The pyramids were not tombs, as many scholars naively
believe," she continued. "In the Solar Mysteries, the candidate
for initiation — after years of preparation — left his body in
a trance-like state for three days in a special pyramid chamber,
while his soul and spirit, accompanied by master Teachers,
went forth to receive higher instruction. During this time, the
physical and etheric bodies could be re-imprinted. When, after

three days, the initiate returned to the physical form, he or she possessed astonishing new visionary and spiritual faculties."

"In today's world," said Celeste, "the process of initiation — that is, the tests, trials and experiences that lead to self-mastery — no longer takes place in temples such as these. Nevertheless, the gates of initiation remain open."

"What do you mean?" I asked.

"I mean," she replied, "that nowadays men and women go through the rigors of self-development and initiation during their everyday life. Experience is the teacher. One may develop the required courage, endurance, resolve, wisdom, and love in the course of ordinary events. Accompanied by a rich inner life of meditation, prayer and reflection, the burning path of individual destiny leads to the development of true spiritual character. This constitutes a genuine path of initiation."

"That's quite a break from ancient tradition," I said.

"Consider it a side benefit of the stresses and difficulties of modern life," said Sabrina, smiling. "Nowadays you can do 'home study,' so to speak." I reflected on the preceding week, the deeper significance of my experiences becoming crystal clear.

After descending the pyramid steps, Chilam and Celeste parted warmly and went their separate ways. Sabrina walked with me awhile, pointing out other features of the lost city. I was particularly amazed by the lush gardens — which boasted an astonishing diversity and beauty. There seemed to be literally hundreds of varieties of fruits and vegetables, many of which I had never seen before. Sabrina perceived what was going though my mind.

"Diversity in nature is exceedingly important," she said. "Nowadays in the industrialized world, agribusiness employs roughly twenty plants for nearly 90% of the world's food. This lack of diversity creates the potential for catastrophe, for these hybridized plants are vulnerable to virtual extinction by food blights, pests and diseases."

"I once read," I commented, "that during the 1845 potato famine in Ireland, a million people died because they relied on a single strain of potato, which became blighted."

Sabrina nodded. "To compound the danger," she continued, "the large corporations raise these plants with heavy amounts of chemicals and often coat the seeds with a pesticide or chemical fertilizer before marketing. These chemicals further deteriorate the soil, destroying delicate life forms and threatening future generations." She pointed to several large buildings which looked like granaries or storage rooms.

"Here in the valley we are stockpiling many non-hybrid seeds which we will reintroduce to the world in the event of major catastrophes. But we're hoping that responsible people within your culture will perceive the danger and take initiative in producing organic seeds, free of agribusiness control."

I thought about Ricardo and Deborah and their small efforts to do exactly what Sabrina was recommending.

We walked quietly for some time before Sabrina left me alone to enjoy the marvels of the valley.

In the late afternoon, I climbed the white steps of the Grecian temple, sat upon a marble bench, and gazed out across the pleasant terrain. A flood of images scrolled across my mind, and I thought of all that had befallen me since discovering the ancient Egyptian relic on the lonely hill overlooking the Pacific. I took the talisman from my pocket and began to examine it carefully. Gazing upon the golden sun with the seven rays, I recalled what Arthur had said about the secret teaching encoded within the medallion's cryptic imagery.

In a flash it occurred to me that all my experiences since leaving the Russian Orthodox chapel had been an unfolding revelation of the medallion's meaning. I was forcefully struck with the realization that Arthur, Sabrina, Celeste, and Chilam had each carefully revealed insights regarding the solar rays, the meanings of which Arthur had explained. My entire experience had, in a sense, been a demonstration of the truths symbolically set into the relic.

I recalled Arthur's words regarding the divine principles of life represented by the solar rays: the Law of Reciprocity or Karma, Supply, Celestial Guidance, Right Relationships, Conscious Evolution, Spiritual Freedom, and Universal Oneness. And the mysterious final secret — which Arthur had said I'd have to discover on my own. Surely it had to do with immortality. My mood unexpectedly changed and a wave of sadness engulfed me. Arthur was gone. Even he was not immortal.

I fell into somber contemplation, but my thoughts grew heavy with resentment. I became angry at the people whose greed for the medallion — for global power — had led to Arthur's death. When I opened my eyes, I saw Sabrina seated beside me.

She handed me a beautiful white robe to wear, the shimmering robe of her order. As I put it on, I tried to place where I had seen the robe before that day. Then I remembered. Arthur had worn it when I saw him in the Basilica of the Virgin of Guadalupe.

"You're troubled about something," Sabrina said softly. "It's Arthur, isn't it?" I bit my lip and nodded.

"Don't blame yourself for what happened," Sabrina said, touching my arm. "Nor even the wicked ones who seem deserving of blame. In these matters leave justice to God. Our task is to rise above the bitterness of earth. In order to love, we must forgive, even those we view as our vilest enemies. Until we forgive, our progress will be hampered. Resentment is an acid to the soul, killing the delicate spiritual blossoms. The power of forgiveness is awesome.

"Arthur's entire life was spent in the service of good. His final sacrifice prevented the medallion from falling into the wrong hands."

"And he saved my life," I said, overcome with gratitude.

"Arthur knew the risk he took. He gave his life consciously so that you might have life, and so that the world would be a better place. Don't think of it as a loss. Arthur's heroic deed raised him to a still greater spiritual height. Through his ex-

traordinary life and his final inspired act, he took a major
initiation...what he often called the deepest secret of the medallion."

"Something to do with immortality?" I asked.

"Each of us is created as an immortal spirit. But our ultimate
goal is to resurrect the atoms of the body, elevating the physical
form to immortal stature, demonstrating completely our mastery of this physical dimension. Thus we spiritualize our material vessel and raise it into the eternal light. This is often
called 'the ascension,' whereby we may function freely upon
any plane of reality from the densest to the most exalted. This
was Arthur's life-long quest and his final achievement.

"After his death in the Basilica, his body was removed to
this hidden valley by members of the Brotherhood of the Star.
The authorities in Mexico City have no idea how it disappeared.
In the sanctity of these temples, Arthur — working in his spirit
body — accomplished the task of transubstantiation...raising
his physical body into an immortal, spiritual condition.

"Now he will enjoy a well-deserved rest upon the inner or
celestial planes, drinking deep from the waters of eternal life.
Should he choose, he may return in order to accomplish even
greater things in loving service to Life. It is through love that
the small self is transcended."

"I'll miss him," I said, tears welling up in my eyes.

"Of course," said Sabrina, smiling serenely. "But do not
mourn for him. He dwells henceforth in the light eternal.

"And remember," counseled Sabrina, "the divine spirit per-
meates all things. If we find the place of love in the depths of
our heart, there is no separation. Time and distance dissolve.
Death is an illusion."

A lovely green and gold butterfly fluttered whimsically
near my face. It dipped and danced between Sabrina and me,
then came to rest on my wrist. I felt a surge of happiness and
laughed aloud. Sabrina laughed with me.

"It's a sign from Arthur!" I cried. "I know he's here." The butterfly flitted from my wrist and softly brushed my cheek, before dancing breezily away.

"I love you, Arthur! I love you!" I whispered, watching the winged creature grow small in the distance.

As the ebbing solar rays of evening struck the pyramid's point, then vanished, I accompanied Sabrina into a great hall beside the Greek temple. She led me to a large, circular table around which were twenty-four chairs. At all but one of them were seated men and women, robed in the vestures of the Brotherhood of the Star. Among them were Chilam and Celeste. One place was empty — save for a vase of violet roses — in honor of Brother Arthur. After a light meal of soup and fruit, Brother Peter arose to address those assembled.

"Dear companions in the light," he began. "Since the dawn of time, the earth has been a classroom set apart by the gods for the race of men to mature toward divine stature. Humanity in its infancy needed close care and guidance. The Great Overlords established the Mystery Schools and glorious temples, similar to the ones in this sacred valley. From these sacred schools came the impulses that guided the races. Through them, the ancient, primordial Wisdom Tradition was expounded by the great Initiates.

"After the fall of Atlantis, it was decreed that the initiate centers gradually withdraw from close association with humanity, for the race had to be weaned of its childlike dependence upon the higher beings.

"The time had come when the individuality in each person must grow to maturity by exercising its own powers of individual judgment and moral choice. Each human being must be able to stand on his own, a free individual. The birth of the divine man must be preceded by the emergence of the independent self, capable of sovereign thought, discrimination and awareness. Each must become his own teacher. The age of unquestioning obedience to a higher authority is over, both in spiritual and material affairs. It is the will of the gods and the Elder Races that each man and woman grow in freedom, unfolding the heroic divine spark from within.

"Now this age draws to a close. We stand upon the threshold of the day of judgment, the separation of the lifewave. The Glorious Ones who hold the evolution of the world and mankind in their care have decreed that, in the age to come, only the deserving may incarnate. The earth shall have a Golden Age; only those may participate who have earned that privilege.

"Those who have learned the law of love and brotherhood will help create a new and majestic civilization. The gates of incarnation shall close to the dark ones, those who would exploit and enslave their fellow beings. There will be a new heaven and a new earth. Already, the first rays of the new day are chasing the darkness.

"In the blessed age of spirit light now dawning, the great truths of life shall once more resonate in the hearts and minds of all. Blessed are they who live these truths. Blessed are they who feed the minds of the young with this knowledge. Understand that Truth, in its fullness, cannot entirely be spoken. Truth, to be known, must be lived. But this much may be said:

"The soul of man is immortal, eternal, deathless. And it shall expand and grow without limit into a thing of sublime loveliness.

"All men and women are the creators of their lives. The destiny of each is unique. All must guide themselves and grow through the sovereignty of self-creation. We are the masters of our fate.

"The eternal, spiritual principle of life is within the soul of each individual, and simultaneously it is in the world, pervading all created things. This eternal Spirit may be perceived and known by those who seek it.

"It needn't take long for the soul to receive illumination if it pursues its goal with determination. Feed the light in the heart by thankfulness and thought divine. Learn to think the thoughts which angels think; then will the inner light grow into a mighty fire. The windows of the soul shall open, revealing the celestial worlds, our true home."

I listened in awe to Peter's words, and I felt the light in my mind expanding. He turned to me and reached out his hand. "Give me the medallion, dear friend. It has journeyed far. Now comes the time for its purification, in preparation for its return to She who authorized its creation."

I carefully removed the relic and handed it to Peter. He set it in a golden, rectangular box which rested in front of him on the table. Then he placed the cover on the box, the handles of which were shaped as angels. I later learned that the box was an amplifier and condenser of spiritual energy, containing extraordinary power. It was a kind of modern Ark of the Covenant, charged with an almost unearthly power generated by the thoughts and will of the greatest Adepts. If a mortal of low vibration or impure motivation were to touch it, he or she would be instantly killed.

Immediately there came a loud crackling and a frightening hiss, then a sound like that of a terrible groan. Sparks flew from the box and a red glow appeared around it. I saw forms, like dark shadows, rise from the box, then dart away — manifestations of human greed and selfish desire which had become attached to the medallion over the ages.

At last all sound ceased. The box assumed its normal appearance. Peter removed the cover and withdrew the dazzling relic. It shone with greater brilliance than ever before. A wave of happiness came over me. I had completed my mission successfully and a ponderous burden fell from my shoulders.

The entire gathering rose and began to sing a sweet anthem. I was so thrilled by the sound that tears came to my eyes. The assemblage slowly filed from the room, leaving Brother Peter, Sabrina and me. The remarkable ceremony left me speechless, a rare thing for me.

"Thanks again, little brother," said Peter with a smile. "Continue putting knowledge into action. In many ways, what you do is more important than what you know. A state of being not expressed in action is like a seed that never sprouts...power unrealized. Don't you agree, Sabrina?"

"Yes," she said, looking at me kindly, "a life of thought not expressed in deeds is like a sun whose rays have no warmth, no power to give life."

The two of them led me to a small room with a couch, a bookcase, and a bed. "Get a good night's rest, dear Jason," Sabrina told me. "Tomorrow will be a busy day, for you've not yet completed your task."

"I'm not sure what you mean," I said, looking first at Sabrina, then Peter. To my dismay, Peter removed the medallion from around his neck and placed it in my hand. "Why are you giving it to me?" I asked, astonished.

"You have one more delivery to make, little courier," he said. "Take the medallion to a young Indian woman who lives not far from Chichén Itzá. Her name is Serafina Flores. Go to the village of Tekom and ask that she have it blessed. You'll understand tomorrow."

"But I thought you were going to give it to Isis, or somebody," I protested. "You know, the Lady of the Medallion." The two of them smiled at me, as if enjoying a mutual secret.

"Get lots of sleep tonight," said Sabrina. "Have you forgotten? Tomorrow is the equinox, September 23rd."

"September 23rd!" I shouted, absolutely dismayed. "I've totally lost track of time! I've got to meet my family tomorrow at Chichén Itzá! But how will I get there? I'm hundreds of miles away, and I haven't seen any cars in these parts!"

"Don't worry, my friend," said Peter. "We'll take care of that. Leave it in the hands of our own private travel agency." Again he smiled mysteriously. I looked at Sabrina. She had an expression of tenderness and love in her eyes. Had I known I was seeing her for the last time, I would have been crushed.

Peter extended his arm, gently placing his hand on my temple. I lost consciousness instantly, falling into a deep, overpowering sleep.

I awoke the next morning — the sun in my face — lying on a large, flat stone. Startled, I saw that I was once again in my Indian clothes. I looked around in confusion, trying to comprehend my whereabouts. The Isis Medallion was in my pocket. In my hand was a red flower, now wilted — the one I had given to Chilam.

Then I knew. I was on the steps of the pyramid at Chichén Itzá, alone again.

Chapter Eleven
REUNION

"A miracle is love made visible." E.J.M.

When my bewilderment passed, I began to climb the pyramid steps, the one known as *El Castillo* — the Castle. My thoughts turned toward the hidden valley and the Brotherhood of the Star. I was thrilled by my experience in the Lost City of Poseid, and amazed at the Brotherhood's miraculous abilities.

Though not comprehending the celestial mechanics which Brother Peter and Sabrina applied to get me to Chichén Itzá, I presumed it was some form of teleportation, taking only moments, for I was rested and refreshed, as if I had slept peacefully through the night.

I reached the top of the large stone structure, a monument to the greatness of the vanished Mayan civilization. Though unused today, it stood as a constant reminder to modern minds of the undiscovered mysteries of our ancient heritage.

Standing at the top of the pyramid, I watched as the first tourists began to arrive that day. One group in particular caught my eye. There were about thirty of them, and they had arrived only minutes after I awoke on the pyramid. For some reason most of them wore white clothing. I saw them make a large circle, holding hands and chanting. I presumed they were a New Age spiritual group, come to Chichén Itzá expressly for the Autumn Equinox in order to participate in some kind of celebration or ritual.

Several hours passed. I became hungry and automatically reached into my pocket. I was thankful to find some of Sabrina's concentrated food. To my delight, I also found one large peso note, worth about a hundred dollars. My friends hadn't abandoned me penniless.

Gazing across the field, I saw three familiar figures walking toward the pyramid. I laughed aloud, and my blood pounded with exhilaration, for I recognized Ricardo and Melissa, with my own divine child, Angelina. I was overjoyed at the prospect of being united with my loved ones.

They were less than fifty yards from the pyramid and I could make out their features. Melissa wore her favorite red dress. She was smiling — her long, dark hair swept by the breeze. Angelina was running happily, wearing a pretty pink skirt. In less than two months she would be four years old.

Walking perhaps thirty yards behind them came three men whose appearances struck me as odd. They all wore dark trousers, light shirts, and sunglasses — looking more like lawyers in the financial district on a lunch break than they did tourists.

My exhilaration dampened. We weren't yet out of the woods. Of course my pursuants would have sent agents to follow Ricardo and my family, believing, quite correctly that they would be led to the object of their hunt. Our reunion would have to be surreptitious. And I would have to conceal my identity from my daughter! If she recognized me, all might still be lost.

I reached into my pocket, finding a few scraps of paper. Nearby, a cluster of tourists were taking pictures and talking. I walked over and asked them, in feigned broken English, for a pen or pencil. A middle-aged woman reached into her purse and gave me a pen. "Are you a Maya?" she asked in a southern drawl.

"Yes...I mean, *si, señora, muchas gracias. Un momento.*" I smiled and bowed slightly, walking away a few steps to scribble some words on the paper. Then I hastily returned the pen.

"May we take your picture, señor?" the lady asked.

"No, gracias," I said, becoming acutely self-conscious.

"What an extraordinary medallion!" the lady said, pointing at me. "Look what this nice Indian man has," she said to her companions. Horrified, I realized that I hadn't placed the jewelled talisman back into its case. It had fallen out of my trouser pocket and dangled from its chain, plainly in view of all. I hurried away from the tourists, nervously stuffing the relic in the case and jamming it unceremoniously into my pocket.

I sat off to one side, my feet dangling over the pyramid's top-most ledge. Several minutes later, the group of tourists began to depart. I cautiously looked around. Melissa was just reaching the top. Ricardo was a half step behind her, carrying Angelina on his shoulders.

This was my chance. I shuffled toward them, my head down. I stopped near Melissa and bent over, pretending to straighten my sandal. As I stood up, I pressed the piece of paper into her hand. I stared into her eyes, hastily covering my mouth with my finger. Melissa glanced at the note, which said:

C'est moi! You're being followed. Not a word to Angelina! Follow me to Tekom. Careful, my love!

From the corner of my eyes I saw her lift her face in my direction and could see the happiness in her eyes. She crumpled the paper and dropped it into her purse.

Melissa whispered to Ricardo. I could tell by the cautious glances he threw in my direction that he knew I was there. By the time the three strange men reached the top, I was headed down the opposite steps.

I wanted us to leave immediately, but that would have aroused suspicion. Chichén Itzá was a major attraction and it would have appeared unusual for Ricardo, Melissa and Angelina to stay only briefly. So for the next five hours we wandered about the ruins of the lost city, visiting the various buildings. I tried to keep Ricardo and my family within view, but remained at a safe distance. Wherever the three of them went, the three, suspicious-looking men followed.

In the afternoon, I strolled toward the parking area, almost a hundred yards ahead of Melissa and the others, scheming how to get to Tekom. Thankfully, I had some pesos.

In the parking lot were several tour buses. A dozen-or-so taxis were waiting to pick up the groups they had brought, and return them to their hotels. A taxi seemed the obvious way to go, but Indians didn't take taxis. Nor could I walk to Tekom. I didn't even know for certain where it was, only that it was a small village near Chichén Itzá. Why hadn't I asked Peter and Sabrina more questions? Why hadn't they given me more advice?

The group of mostly white-clad pilgrims were streaming into the parking area, congregating near a tour bus. I was drawn to them like a magnet, and stood a few feet away, eavesdropping on their conversations. They looked like Americans and their speech left no doubt! They were a mixed group, happy and good-natured, with women outnumbering the men by two to one. I was convinced it was some New Age group, drawn to Chichén Itzá because of its reputation as a global power spot.

A slender, dark-haired, elderly woman, apparently the group leader, gathered the pilgrims together in a semi-circle. Her speech at first was indistinct — something about departure. Then she spoke loudly, words which made my heart leap.

"All right, everyone. Next stop, Tekom. All aboard." Tekom! Blessed Serendipity!

"Excuse me, please," I said to the dark-haired leader. "May I come with you as far as Tekom?" She looked at me, slightly surprised, as if she hadn't expected me to speak English. Her features gave the impression of goodwill, the kind of person you could trust in a pinch.

"I'm in a bit of a jam," I said. "I'd be happy to pay you." I thrust the paper money in her face.

"That's all right, child," she said, laughing good-naturedly. Her voice was sweet and slightly southern. "The money's not important. I see no reason why not. We'll be happy to give you a ride." I coudn't believe my good fortune. The thought flashed in my mind — could Sabrina and Peter have had a hand in this?

The bus-driver made his appearance and some of the pilgrims began to board the bus. Ricardo and my family were entering the parking area, followed closely by the grim-looking threesome. Making sure Ricardo saw me, I nodded almost imperceptibly toward the bus. He walked over immediately.

"I couldn't help noticing you out there by the monuments today," Ricardo said, to no one in particular. I smiled to myself. He was a gregarious sort and would begin a conversation with anyone. "You must be Americans."

"How could you guess?" said a stocky, short-haired woman, laughing mildly.

"Did you come for the equinox?" Ricardo asked.

"That's right," she answered. "The world needs healing, and the power spots are sensitive areas in which to make contact with Mother Earth. The equinox is a time of heightened receptivity. The energies here are beautiful, aren't they?"

"Magnificent," said Ricardo. "Where're you going next?"

"To Tekom," chimed in a tall, thin, gray-haired man. "There's an Indian woman supposedly having visions of the Blessed Mother, so we thought we'd check it out."

"May we come?" asked Ricardo, not missing a beat. "There's just the three of us." He gestured at Melissa and Angelina, who by this time had come up beside him.

"I'll ask Arlene," said the stocky woman. As she turned toward the dark-haired group leader, my gaze fell upon my daughter. I had avoided looking at her all day, but I could no longer resist. She was so beautiful, so sweet, so innocent. She was Heaven's child.

"That'll be fine," I heard Arlene say. "They can come along with this nice Indian man." I felt her look my way, and the glances of the group fell upon me. I stared adoringly at Angelina, entranced, betraying all caution. Angelina's gaze followed the others. She turned and peered squarely into my eyes.

"Daddy!" she exclaimed.

At once, the three men sprang forward, drawing handguns from their coats. I dashed frantically toward the bus — losing instantly my hard-won spiritual composure — nearly knocking over an elderly woman.

"Get that man!" came a shout from behind. "He's wanted by the C.I.A.!"

"Protect him!" Ricardo yelled. "These jerks are the criminals."

"Get the girl!" a gruff voice shouted.

"Mommy!" came my daughter's cry.

Melissa screamed. "Don't let them take my baby! Don't let them take my girl!" I was crouched on the floor of the bus, in a cold sweat. I stood up, ashamed, and resolved that they would not harm my daughter.

Shouts came from outside. There was a loud, sickening thud, and Ricardo groaned. He had grabbed one of the agent's arms, who then clubbed him in the head with a pistol butt. He dropped to his hands and knees.

Arlene, the dark-haired leader, raised both her hands above her head, as if invoking peace from the skies. The pilgrims formed a semi-circle around her, a few steps from Melissa and the fallen Ricardo. The three agents stood several feet away. One of them gripped Angelina tightly by the wrist. I came to the door of the bus, holding my hands in the air.

"Leave the child alone," I commanded, stepping down. I pushed past the white-clad pilgrims. Walking in front of Melissa, I looked into her fathomless brown eyes, wet with tears, then stopped a few feet from the three agents.

"Do whatever you want with me," I said, "but you'd better let the girl go now." There was a new power in my voice, an unshakable resolution.

The one holding Angelina let her go and she ran into Melissa's arms.

"Please don't go away again, daddy," she said. I winced at her words.

"You can put your guns away," I said to the agents. "Nobody here is armed."

"Give us the medallion," said one of them, apparently the leader. He had a scar across his cheek — the stereotypical bad-guy. He thrust his hand toward me and I reached into my pocket, touching the talisman. The three agents pointed their guns at my heart.

"Don't try anything," the leader growled, "or you'll end up like your priest friend at the church in Mexico City."

Slowly, carefully, I removed the medallion from my pocket, lifting it into the air. The agent hesitantly extended one arm toward mine, fixing me with his stare, gun in his other hand. The golden goddess flashed in the Mexican sun.

Momentarily, awareness of my surroundings vanished. A bizarre light, a luminous mist, formed above me, and I sensed a sweet and lovely presence. It was the mysterious Lady whose beauty had so inspired me twice before when I had worn the medallion around my neck. Her image was faint, indefinite, yet my soul was thrilled.

Then she vanished, and I saw another image, hostile and terrifying. I recognized the being whose surface beauty veiled an unspeakable malice. The spectre's gleaming eyes became visible, cold as dark jewels. I sensed an overpowering desire, a burning lust for the medallion, issue from the phantom. A tangible breath of hatred swept over me and I thought I would faint. I clutched the medallion with all my strength, refusing to let it go.

The agent roughly grabbed my arm and I regained external sight. He thrust his gun in his jacket, then produced a pair of handcuffs. I gripped the medallion tightly in both my hands.

"Let him go," said a commanding voice from a few feet behind the agents. They blocked my vision and I could not see who was speaking.

"Do not harm him," the stranger said again. "No one may take what is not rightfully his." His voice made me tremble, disbelieving. The three agents turned around to see who had the audacity to challenge them.

There stood an imposing figure, clothed regally in the white robe of the Brotherhood of the Star, glimmering in the sun. "Arthur!" I whispered, awestruck. The old priest stood silently, appearing as he did the day he was shot in the Basilica of the Virgin of Guadalupe.

The agents stepped back nervously, also recognizing Arthur from the cathedral.

"Jeez!" one of them said. "Who is this guy, superman?" Their guns were trained on Arthur's heart.

Arthur looked at me and smiled. "Remember this, Jason. Divine Love contains the greatest mystery. Through love is death transcended." I stared at him wonderingly. "Behold," he said, "the final secret of the medallion." Although Arthur appeared in his familiar form, a peculiar glow shone around him and he emanated a transcendent, otherworldly peace.

"I know you don't want to be delayed," he said, looking first at me, then at Melissa and the New Agers. "You may get back on the bus now."

"The hell they may!" said an agent angrily. "No damn ghost is gonna push us around. This time we'll finish you and you'll burn in..."

Before he could go on, there was a searing flash of light. Arthur's form turned a brilliant gold, resplendent as the sun. The three agents cried out and fell, blinded, to the earth. We shielded our eyes, unable to look directly at Arthur.

"Go, my friends," he said. "Have no fear. Through love, miracles are accomplished. The light of God never fails." The brilliance of Arthur's presence grew still more lucid, then he vanished. On the ground where he had stood, the three agents groveled, unable to see.

"Let's go, everyone," said Arlene, lowering her arms. The pilgrims, led by Arlene, helped Ricardo to his feet and ushered us onto the bus. Then they slowly filed in after. The agents lay in the dust where they had fallen. Moments later, we were on the road to Tekom.

Chapter Twelve
SERAFINA FLORES

*"Faith is the bird that feels the light and sings
when the dawn is still dark."* —Tagore

A solemn silence blanketed the bus. Melissa and I embraced for a long moment, letting our eyes speak. We sat near the front with Ricardo. After a moment's hesitation, Angelina climbed into my arms, holding me tightly. The New Agers didn't know what to make of us, nor of the events they had just witnessed. The only words came in whispers.

I glanced back once and saw several cars, presumably with more agents, forming a bizarre parade behind us.

It seemed only minutes before we were on the outskirts of the little village. Our driver pulled the bus onto a narrow dirt lane, beside which were a cluster of small, nondescript houses. To our surprise, a crowd of several hundred people surrounded the homes, with one in particular apparently the object of their interest. The crowd parted as the driver pulled the bus within a few dozen yards of the house.

"Eet's here, amigos," he said. "Thees is the place."

"Well, dear stranger, you made it," someone said, placing a gentle hand on my shoulder. I turned to see Arlene, a glowing smile on her face. "Let me know if we can be of any more help to you. Those C.I.A. types sure have got it in for you. But I see that you already have heavenly protection. I've witnessed many strange and wonderful things in my life, but that about tops everything. Who was that man? Or should I say angel?"

I shook my head, still awestruck by the experience.

"Something like an angel, to be sure. I'll have to tell you another time, when I fully understand it myself. At the moment, we need to find the home of Serafina Flores. Do you have any idea where..."

"Serafina?" said Arlene, with a look of surprise. "Why, you're here, child. Serafina's the visionary."

The white-clad New Agers piled off the bus, making a cordon around the door for Ricardo, my family and me. We stepped into the sultry air, pressed through the throng of people, and knocked on the door of Serafina's house.

A sweet-faced girl of about seventeen years opened the door. I held up the relic in front of her. "We've come to get Serafina's blessing," I said. "We've been sent here and we need..." The girl smiled, took my arm, and gently pulled me into the house. Melissa, Ricardo and Angelina followed.

"Come in," she said in Spanish. "I've been expecting you." She closed the door behind us and introduced herself. Her name — Serafina Flores.

Serafina was petite and attractive, and her dark, penetrating eyes danced with a secret light. Her pretty, heart-shaped face seemed older and wiser than her seventeen years. Like so many Indian women of the region, the contours of her mouth seemed perpetually ready to give birth to a smile. She had a charming, gracious manner. "*Mi casa es su casa,*" she told us.

There were only four rooms in her dwelling, a combination kitchen-dining area, a sitting room, and two small bedrooms. She introduced us to her mother, Conchita, and her three younger sisters; her father had recently passed away. Conchita was preparing dinner, and to our surprise, we were invited.

"Please sit down," Serafina told us. "It's a pleasure to meet you." Melissa's Spanish was even better than mine, and it was Ricardo's native tongue, so we had no problem communicating.

Fortunately, Ricardo was not badly hurt. He had a large bruise and a knot on his head, but the skin was only slightly broken. He sat in an old wicker chair, polishing his spectacles with his handkerchief, looking the part of a professorial Indiana Jones. Melissa and I, with Angelina, collapsed on a couch upholstered with floral cotton pillows.

"Thank you so much, Serafina," I said. "Please forgive us for intruding on you like this. When you say you were expecting us, I'm not sure what you mean."

Serafina smiled sweetly. She seemed modest, almost shy. "What I mean is that the Blessed Lady told me to expect four Americans, one of them a child. She told me they would be bringing something.

"Each day when Our Lady calls me, I go to where she leads." Serafina pointed outside. "There she gives me a few words to tell the people. Then I offer her these objects which the people bring me." She gestured toward a small wooden table, covered with a white embroidered cloth, on which was set a bouquet of fresh-cut flowers. The table was laden with objects, many of them religious in nature, such as rosaries. But there were also many jewelry pieces, pendants, chains, rings, watches, and so forth. "The Blessed Mother," continued Serafina, "kisses each one to bless it. She told me you would be bringing something important to have blessed."

"Yes, Serafina," I said. "We've brought this." I removed the ancient talisman from its case and gave it to her. She took it gently in her hands, admired it for a moment, then placed it lovingly on the table with the other articles.

"It is beautiful," she said softly.

Serafina told us that her visions had begun unexpectedly about three weeks earlier. She had been gathering flowers in the fields by the village church to take to her mother, who was ill. She heard a voice ringing in her mind, words spoken clearly and distinctly, yet inaudible to her ears. She called it "a voiceless voice." The unknown speaker told her to come the next day to the orange tree in the field by her house at noon, and to bring her mother with her.

"But my mother is bed-ridden!" she had protested.

The voice told her that her mother would be well in the morning, then said matter-of-factly that it was Mary, Mother of Jesus, who spoke.

The next morning, Serafina's mother, Conchita, who had been running a high fever and hadn't been out of bed for five days, was completely healed. News spread rapidly of the "miracle," and about a dozen people had gone with Serafina and her mother that day to the orange tree.

Exactly at noon, Serafina had fallen on her knees to the ground, gazing skyward, in an ecstatic trance. The Blessed Mother appeared visibly to her for the first time, speaking in a voice which only she could hear, saying she would be giving her instruction in the weeks to come. She had said that she should pray more fervently, for a great danger was coming upon the world. Then she said she would leave a sign so that all would know Serafina was telling the truth.

Serafina's ecstasy ended, and when she got to her feet she told the onlookers — who had seen and heard nothing — what she'd witnessed in the vision. Some of them doubted her, but all then noticed that the orange tree was in full blossom. It was especially miraculous in that the tree had not bloomed nor borne fruit in five years.

The news spread like wildfire through the district and Serafina's little house had become a place of pilgrimage and veneration overnight. The eager crowds came each day and followed her to the little orange tree to witness her ecstasy. Many gave her objects for the Madonna to kiss.

Ricardo, Melissa and I looked wonderingly at each other, aware of how providential was the guidance that had led us.

The crowd outside, many of them pilgrims from hundreds of miles away, camped near Serafina's house. Among them were members of the media. Our adversaries had to be very careful; we felt that we'd be safe through the night.

Seated around the wooden dining table, we shared a delicious dinner of enchiladas with the family. Afterwards, Serafina spoke to numerous people who came to ask for her prayers and blessing. She modestly asserted that she could, of herself, do nothing, insisting that she was in no way special.

After helping her mother put her siblings to bed, Serafina sat down with us again on the small couch and chairs in the sitting room.

"Can you tell us the message that Mother Mary is giving you to tell the world?" asked Melissa.

Serafina smiled sweetly and nodded, her dark eyes illumined by the light of her thoughts. "The Blessed Lady tells us that a great chastisement is coming upon the earth. She said we must pray constantly for ourselves and for others...especially for the children and young people because their minds are being injured by drugs and harmful ideas. Many people are in danger of losing their souls and their spiritual life.

"Her heart is full of sorrow for the great suffering that is about to come upon the people of this planet. I have seen her weeping. The Church suppresses or distorts her words, and the media ridicules her messengers. The world is not heeding the warnings.

"She says that her message is for all people. She is the Heavenly Mother of all, not just Catholics. She has even told me that she herself is not Catholic, though I am afraid to tell this to my priest." Serafina blushed slightly, then crossed herself.

"Can the chastisement be stopped?" Ricardo asked.

Serafina's eyes were sad. "Santa Maria says it's possible to lessen the hardship if people pray enough and change in their hearts. Otherwise, much suffering must come upon the nations. The hearts of the people have been hardened. The leaders of the governments and the men of science have wicked thoughts. They think only of power, money and destruction."

"What will happen in the chastisement?" I asked, thinking back to what both Sabrina and Peter had said about the need for karmic cleansing, and an imminent planetary purification.

"There will be a sequence of events that will bring each nation to its knees," answered Serafina. "Suffering such as people have never known before. The earthquakes will increase and will be in all countries. Eventually they will be of monstrous size, causing the destruction of many great cities. Volcanoes will erupt across the land and beneath the seas. There will be new volcanoes created. The earth will violently shake, and mountains will collapse. Much land will sink beneath the waves, especially coastal areas. In your country of America, both coasts will be destroyed...first in California, then in the east. Yet new land will rise from the ocean floor, regions that existed in previous times.

"Floods will be vast, while in some areas there will be terrible droughts and not a drop of water to drink. Hurricanes, tornadoes and all manner of storms will be of unimaginable size and fury. Great tidal waves will wash away multitudes. At times, huge forest fires will rage out of control. The atmosphere will change, becoming dark, due to the many volcanoes. Food crops will be lost, resulting in famine and severe shortages.

"The global economy will falter," she added, "and the systems of currency will collapse. This will bring most governments to their knees."

"What about war?" Melissa asked. We both looked over at Angelina, asleep on a beautiful knitted blanket. We were relieved that she could not hear the conversation.

"There will not be a third world war, although there will be savage conflict in many places. It is Mother Nature herself who will wage war against people."

"Why is that?" I asked.

Serafina paused a moment, her dark eyes glistening. "The Blessed Mother tells me that these upheavals of nature are symptoms — that is, effects. The cause is our cruelty to living things and each other. Men are destroying the earth with pollution, chemicals, and greed. Santa Maria says that the earth is alive, and must react violently in order to save herself. We have forgotten that the earth is also our mother."

We were quiet for some time before Ricardo spoke up. "If all these things are coming about, Serafina, how can we prepare?"

"The Blessed Mother tells me that most important is the preparation in our hearts and minds through prayer and meditation. Stay attuned to the spirit by prayer and thanksgiving as Native Americans have always done. Any kind of prayer is good, and will be effective if we are sincere. We must learn to pray always... without ceasing. In this way, we unite with God in our hearts and our minds.

"She has told me many times that if we stay uplifted in our thoughts and feelings, we will rise above the difficulties and they will not harm us. Although the natural changes will be vast, the greatest upheavals will be inward, as people release old patterns of fear, hate and negation and open to a new world of beauty, love and joy. This is our spiritual birthright.

"She says we must seek to heal all our relationships and begin to heal our families. If all the families of the world would begin to heal, then all communities, all nations and eventually the world would be healed."

"I understand that our inner preparation is the most important concern," I said. "But shouldn't we be doing other things as well?"

"Yes, it is wise to make practical preparations also."

"For instance?" asked Melissa.

"The coming changes will touch the whole world. There is no place to run and hide. Naturally, some places will be safer than others. Santa Maria has told me we should think about how we will get food and water when the shortages come. She said it's wise to plan ahead and store provisions. That way we will be in a position not only to help our loved ones, but others as well. Food seeds will also be of great importance — especially those seeds that can reproduce each year. Those who make no preparations will be dependent upon the generosity of others."

Serafina paused for a moment, as if she wasn't sure how to continue. "Eventually," she said softly, "we will receive assistance from angels, and also people who come from other planets and stars." Ricardo, Melissa and I exchanged glances, surprised at Serafina's assertion.

"Extra-terrestrials?" Ricardo asked, not bothering to conceal his astonishment. Serafina smiled shyly and nodded. It occurred to me that there must have been a lot of things difficult for Serafina to confide to her priest.

Ricardo was sitting at the edge of the wicker chair, riveted by Serafina's words. "If all these things come about," he said, "there's going to be absolute chaos. Nobody I know is thinking seriously about this kind of a scenario. Even the so-called advanced nations will be at risk. Right now the United States government maintains only about a thirty-day supply of wheat in the event of national emergency. It will take extraordinary cooperation to survive."

Serafina's large eyes acknowledged Ricardo's remarks. "Santa Maria wants people to know that we must learn to live together," she said. "Community is necessary; we must care for each other. She says that only those who have love in their hearts, and who practice love, will survive. It is the end of the age."

"How long do we have before these things start happening?" Melissa asked.

"We are now in the midst of the tribulations. The changes will increase in frequency and magnitude. By the dawn of the new century, they will be largely finished. We will then have an entirely new planet. The chastisement will have been accomplished." Serafina hung her head slightly, as if pondering the weight of the message she had been chosen to give.

After a moment's silence, Serafina smiled radiantly. "She also says we must learn to find joy in our hearts, even during the tribulations. The coming events will be for the good of the world. The darkness and hatred of human beings will be removed by the changes. Many of the worthy ancient cultures, such as the Mayan, will re-emerge. We shall enter a Golden Age of Peace and Prosperity, an age of Wisdom. The Blessed Lady calls it 'the aftertime.'

"She has told me it will be a time when men and women will be seen as spiritual equals. Women will be honored as expressions of the Heavenly Queen. They will be leaders in the coming world. For this reason, there is cause for happiness. I only feel sad when I think of the children who must live through the time of great suffering." She looked at Angelina with a tender expression, then stood up.

"I'm sorry I have no better place for you to sleep." She looked around her at the floor and couch.

"For us it will be the finest of palaces," Ricardo said.

We said goodnight to Serafina and prepared for sleep. Serafina had provided us refuge and security for the night, but her message had turned our world upside down.

Chapter Thirteen
THE LADY OF THE MEDALLION

"Darkness needs hate in order to live;
Evil dies when we forgive." E.J.M.

A loud knock on the door awoke us. The sun had barely risen, and it seemed too early for visitors. The knocking came again, this time more brazenly.

"We must speak with Serafina Flores," came a voice in Spanish, a trifle rude.

Serafina appeared at the door as we folded our blankets and wiped the sleep from our eyes. When she opened it, three priests entered — Jesuits — accompanied by a man who looked like a government official.

"Señorita," said a priest, "that man has stolen something that belongs to Mother Church." The priest pointed in my direction. "It must be returned to us immediately. Otherwise you are assisting him in his crime, which is a grave sin."

One of the priests stood quietly to the side. He spoke softly in English to the government official. I sat bolt upright, then jumped to my feet. The English-speaking priest turned and glared at me. It was Brother Reynard.

"Please, Fathers, these people are my guests," pleaded Serafina. "I beg that you leave them alone."

"Very well, my child," said the Spanish-speaking Jesuit. "We will not bother them, although I believe the Mexican police and the authorities are seeking them. Just give us the object which he stole from the Church and we will not trouble you further." Brother Reynard took a step into the house, brushing past Serafina and walking abruptly toward the table on which lay the medallion. I stepped between him and the table.

"Rather rude of you to burst in like this, isn't it, Father?" I said. I no longer feared him, feeling only a fierce contempt. It was all I could do to check my anger and remain poised.

"Well, well, well, my tricky little jay-bird," sneered Reynard. "You've eluded us so far, but it does look sadly as if you've reached the end of the road." Reynard's smile was sinister, loathsome. "Look what your shenanigans did to poor Brother Arthur. Tsk, tsk. You should feel shame at the tragedy you've created."

"It's people like you, Reynard," I said fiercely, "who spilled his blood. His death is on your hands and theirs. Arthur was a hero, a martyr and a saint. But you, Brother Reynard...you're nothing but the devil's proxy."

Reynard's face grew red and he became visibly enraged. He grabbed my arm and tried to shove me from his path. I clutched the crucifix hanging from his neck. He spat in my face, then drew a dagger from his robe. Conchita and the children gasped.

"Be careful, Jason!" Melissa screamed.

Reynard raised the dagger and I lunged backwards, snapping the chain. The crucifix fell, clattering, to the floor. The enraged priest swiped at me, missing wildly. Then he plunged toward the table. Ricardo shouted and stepped toward him. The other priests, along with the official in the business suit, pushed past Serafina; one of them tackled Ricardo. Conchita, with the children, cowered in the kitchen.

Melissa ran for the table and grasped the medallion an instant before Brother Reynard. Reynard raised his arm — dagger in hand — ready to strike her. His arm froze in mid-air.

"My arm! I can't move my arm!" He shouted, wincing in pain. I stepped past him and Melissa handed me the relic. Then I hurried to Serafina and placed it around her neck. Reynard slumped in a chair, grimacing painfully, his arm fully extended. Ricardo removed the dagger from the priest's clenched fist.

By this time, a large crowd of pilgrims had gathered at the door, concerned for Serafina's well-being. She spoke quietly, trying to reassure them.

The expression on her face unexpectedly changed, as if she were listening to a faraway sound. "She is calling me," she said calmly. "I must go at once to the orange tree. Please bring the articles to be blessed by the Virgin." She turned toward

Ricardo, Melissa and me. "Come now, and stay close by my side."

I picked up Angelina and the four of us stepped outside, walking behind Serafina. The crowd cleared a small path and surged with us toward the orange tree at the end of the field, about a hundred yards away.

The pilgrims had roped off a large area around the tree so that Serafina would not be pushed or jostled during her ecstacy. We had learned, however, that she was entirely oblivious to external happenings while in trance.

In the crowd, I noticed the white-clad New Agers who had helped us so miraculously the previous day. There were also numerous people associated with the print media, radio and even one television crew. Also scattered among the crowd were the agents who had followed us from Chichén Itzá. Their number had apparently swollen during the night, for there seemed to be dozens of them. Then I saw a face that stunned me.

A man in a blue business suit, carrying his jacket out of respect for the sultry heat, was among those closest to Serafina. He saw me and we glowered at each other as we walked. We could have reached out our arms and touched each other.

"Good morning, Dr. Bundy," I said, grinning broadly. "What a surprise to find you so far from home. Were you looking for something? Something perhaps you would kill for?" I stared directly into his cold, hard eyes. As with Brother Reynard, I felt no fear of the man or those he represented — only a towering contempt for the darkness in their hearts. He spoke not a word, but the rage was clearly etched on every line of his face.

Some in the crowd began to chant a lovely devotional hymn. The look of reverence in their eyes contrasted sharply with the cynicism on the faces of the scoffers — and the greed of those seeking the medallion.

"Peace be with you," I said to Dr. Bundy. The words when they formed in my mind were bitter with cynicism, but before they left my tongue, a beneficent presence touched my heart. I spoke sincerely, unexpectedly uplifted by the majestic mood of the moment to a state of mind transcending rivalry and antagonism. I was moved beyond hatred to a place where I saw the futility of revenge. I felt only pity for the Reynards and Bundys of the world, unable to rise above their greed for domination over others.

We reached the orange tree and Serafina stepped beneath the rope into the grassy area set apart for her. To my surprise, she took hold of my arm, insisting that I enter with her. She gestured to Ricardo and Melissa to do the same. Two other men entered the special area, carrying with them the articles belonging to the faithful. Around Serafina's neck hung the relic of Isis, dazzling in the Mexican sun.

Serafina was praying silently, fervently. Others in the crowd did the same. Then I saw something that brought tears of wonder to my eyes. Although there was no wind, the leaves of the orange tree began to rustle softly. One large branch bent down, as if something or someone were resting upon it. I blinked in amazement, for it appeared that there was a soft, fleecy cloud around and under the branch.

Serafina uttered a mild gasp, then fell to her knees, her head straight back. Ecstasy! A cry of wonder arose from the onlookers and many began to weep, continuing their fervent prayers. Serafina's hands were clasped together, and the look on her face was the sweetest, most transcendent and inspiring I had ever beheld.

She remained in quiet, ecstatic trance for several minutes. At times her lips moved, as if in prayer, or perhaps simply speaking to the unseen Lady. Then Serafina slowly rose to her feet. She turned toward the two men holding the articles to be blessed, and without looking, began picking up one after another, offering them to be kissed by the invisible Presence. Then she returned each to the two men standing at her side.

When at last every item had been blessed, she slowly lifted the treasured Egyptian amulet from her breast and raised it aloft. To our surprise, she let go of the relic and dropped her hands slightly. Yet the medallion remained suspended in the air! The astonished onlookers uttered a collective gasp, then fell mute with wonder.

The soft, fleecy cloud began slowly to rise, until it was several feet above the orange tree. The Medallion of Isis rose with the cloud, remaining several feet above it, as if held by the invisible Lady. The pilgrims gazed in awe at the strange spectacle.

"Look! The sun!" someone shouted. All eyes turned eastward. The golden disc of the sun, still low in the morning sky, had turned a deep, crimson red. To our amazement, we could look at it directly without shielding our eyes.

The crimson orb began to spin in the sky and to cast off brilliant colors of every imaginable hue and shade. Many in the crowd who had been standing fell to their knees, weeping, praying, and begging forgiveness from the heavenly powers. Then, abruptly, the sun stood still again, retaining its crimson glow.

The medallion's brilliance grew more intense, becoming nearly too luminous to look upon. A breeze blew through the meadow, whipping up the branches of the orange tree, yet the talisman remained motionless.

Then a flash of light lit up the grove with an incandescence greater than that of the sun. A cry of fear and wonder arose from the crowd. Not a man, woman or child remained standing. I closed my eyes an instant from the glare; when I opened them again, the Medallion of Isis had vanished!

In that moment my inner vision was opened, and I beheld the Lady in all her splendor. The Blessed Mother stood with gentle countenance, bathed in a corona of brilliant light, an unspeakably beautiful smile gracing her lips. She was dressed in shimmering white and blue, her hands outstretched in blessing, supported in a cloud. Her garments seemed to be formed of living light, as if she were adorned with rays of the sun. From her right hand was draped the Medallion of Isis.

Before my spellbound gaze, the Queen of Heaven changed form. Suddenly she wore garments of a bygone age, her dark hair framing her beautiful face. Around and above her head shone a golden disc, luminous as the sun. Behind her stretched wings of gold and blue. She smiled at me with infinite sweetness. Grace and Mercy streamed, living, from her eyes. She was Isis, Heaven's Queen, most beloved of the ancient world.

I realized intuitively that the radiant Lady of Light took many other forms to express Herself to humankind, as it pleased her. These included goddesses of the East with whom I was familiar, as well as ancient personifications no longer worshipped by present-day mankind. She was the eternal Sophia — Wisdom Herself — manifest throughout the ages.

Slowly Isis faded from view and she became again the glorious Madonna. She was the luminous, loving Queen of Heaven, the eternal Mother of the World in a modern form. Isis and Madonna were one and the same — Mother Goddess of the race, Celestial Queen.

As I knelt, tears streaming down my cheeks, I thanked her ceaselessly in silent prayer. She gave a gesture of benediction, conveying limitless love and kindness. Then she slowly vanished from view. The medallion had returned to Whom it belonged, beyond the reach of mortal hands. My task was complete. I was free.

The crowd rose to its feet in silent wonder. Then they gave a triumphant shout, lifting Serafina on their shoulders. They carried the smiling visionary back to her house, singing, and praising God for the awesome miracle.

On the ground nearby knelt Ulysses Bundy, head down, staring vacantly. His quest for the medallion had ended. Perhaps another, more noble, had begun.

I picked up Angelina in my arms and we walked with the crowd toward the rising sun.

Chapter Fourteen
HOMEWARD BOUND

"Every human being is a spark
that wants to burst into flame." —Reshad Feild

"Quite a view!" Melissa said, reaching over and squeezing my hand. I looked out the window of the Boeing 707, cruising at thirty thousand feet above the Mexican terrain. "We'll be in Mexico City in an hour," I said.

"And tomorrow, it's home sweet home," chimed in Ricardo from the seat on my left. "How does that feel, my friend?"

"I'm not sure I can put it into words," I answered. "It's not often that I'm speechless."

"I have to admit, Jason. You're a rare bird," Ricardo said.

Melissa toyed with my wedding band. "An endangered species," she added.

"Thankfully, not extinct," I said.

"I always knew," said Melissa, "there was something of the caveman in you. Just promise me this, Jason. No more adventures — at least not for a while. I'm not the Amelia Earhart type."

"At least not for a while," I said. "I'm beat. I've forgotten what it's like to spend a normal evening around the house." Although I'd been in Mexico less than two weeks, it seemed an eternity. I realized, despite my words, that my life would never be ordinary again; I had changed too much inside. Like the butterfly, I could never crawl back into my cocoon.

"If what Serafina says is true," said Ricardo, "about the coming earth changes, we just might have to ban the word 'normal' from our vocabularies, at least for the rest of this decade." He pointed to a newspaper headline in Spanish, reporting a major earthquake in Turkey.

"Those poor people," winced Melissa.

"We've poisoned Mother Earth and she is convulsing," said Ricardo.

"Better get a compass," I said. "We'll be sailing uncharted waters the next few years."

Melissa sighed and gazed out the window. "Oh brave new world," I heard her whisper.

I put my arm around Melissa and held her tightly. She handed me the lapis love token which I had lost — then found — on the Pacific hills just two weeks before. As I put it around my neck, I felt we were beginning our relationship anew. It seemed my life itself — the ultimate gift — was being returned to me.

"I missed you, love," I said, kissing Melissa on the cheek.

"I missed you, too," she said. There was a pause. "At least ...some of the time." She smiled teasingly. "I hope you learned a few things out there in the forest," she continued.

"You mean, about relationships?" I asked.

Melissa smiled. "As I recall," she said, "you did promise to get some counseling."

"Me Tarzan; you Jane," I whispered.

"I'm anxious to get out of the jungle, Jason."

"Let's walk together," I said.

Angelina crawled into my lap as Melissa shared her experiences during my absence. In many respects, she had gone through as much as me.

"I'm a stronger person for weathering these storms," she said. "But being strong is not enough. Someone very special needs our love." She stroked Angelina's curly hair.

"We all need each other's love," I said.

"That's why we're here," smiled Melissa. She gently took my hand.

I felt a stirring in my heart as we talked about listening — of rekindled feelings — and about communicating with candor and trust.

I told Melissa of my experiences with Sabrina, Chilam, Celeste and Arthur — the guides on my soul's journey. At last, I was coming out of the dark woods.

We fell silent for a time, reflecting on our experiences in Mexico. After the miracle at the orange tree, we had spent a few hours with Serafina, then hitched a ride with Arlene and our New Age friends on their bus, heading toward Mérida. From Mérida we got on the first available flight to Mexico City.

We had learned that Brother Reynard and the other Jesuits had followed the crowd to the orange tree. Reynard's arm had remained frozen in a painfully extended position until the moment of the brilliant flash, when the relic had disappeared from view. Bystanders heard him publicly confessing his sins and begging forgiveness. We felt we had no more to fear from either Bundy or Reynard.

We had also learned that, although many witnesses had seen the vision of the Madonna, apparently only a few pilgrims, along with Ricardo, Melissa and me, had shared the perception of the Blessed Mother becoming Isis, then transforming once again. The Heavenly Queen had not chosen to reveal this sacred mystery to all those present, most likely out of respect for their current belief systems.

Upon reflection, I knew that the radiant Being whose presence I had seen and felt while wearing the ancient relic was truly the Lady of the Medallion herself, the Universal Mother, Isis-Sophia-Madonna. For all time to come I would think of her as the Queen of the Sun.

I think my greatest happiness came when I thought of Arthur. My pain and loss at his passing had vanished, replaced by a quiet joy, an inner knowing. Arthur had mastered the profoundest mysteries of the medallion, revealing its secrets in his life, ultimately defeating the final enemy, death itself. He had shown us that the goal of human endeavor was glorious beyond description.

Upon arrival at the Mexico City airport, we went into the terminal to change flights. We would have to go through customs and my major concern was not having my passport, which I had left with Santos' family in the Yucatan village.

After confirming our flight, we walked toward the international departure gate, scanning all the faces.

"Still running for your life, are you, Jason?" I turned and saw Veronica's beaming smile. Beside her was Salvador. We had called them from Mérida the previous day, telling them of our brief stopover at the airport.

"Now I'm running *with* my life," I answered, giving her a warm embrace. "It's a much better feeling." Ricardo and Veronica hugged, and I introduced Melissa and Angelina to Veronica and Salvador.

"You made a good catch," Veronica said to Melissa, winking.

"He's a bit like wine," Melissa answered. "Improving with age."

Veronica handed me a small, brightly-colored, woven bag. "I was told you might be needing this," she said. I looked inside and found my passport, notebooks, Russian Orthodox gown and cross, Arthur's flashlight, and a few other personals.

"How'd you get these?" I asked, amazed.

"A dark-haired woman came by just five minutes ago," Veronica explained, "and handed them to us, saying to give them to you. She didn't even say who she was."

"Sabrina!" I exclaimed.

"You really get around, young man," Salvador said with a wink. "You'll have to write a book one day."

"Not a chance," I said. "Nobody would believe me."

"My advice, for what it's worth," said Veronica, "is to stay out of the jewelry business."

"And the courier business!" Ricardo added.

"At the moment, I'm out of business, period. I'm broke, and don't have a job."

Melissa grasped my hand. "What you have," she said, "is far more valuable." I picked up Angelina and gave her a kiss.

We spoke for a few more minutes with Veronica and Salvador, then we bade each other farewell. "Next time...Acapulco!" I shouted back at them. It wasn't easy to say goodbye.

We went through customs without a hitch and boarded the jet bound for San Francisco. It was comforting to know that George Fort, whom we had telephoned, would be waiting at the airport to greet us.

In the air once more, I rummaged through the brightly-colored bag of personal belongings from Sabrina, given to me by Veronica just minutes earlier. My eye fell upon a piece of folded paper taped to Arthur's flashlight. I took it out and opened it. It was a hand-written note which said:

Well done, dear Jason!
    You've earned a rest. But we're not finished with you just yet. Are you still willing? We'll be in touch!
                Best wishes, Sabrina.

My head fell back against the seat. I sighed and smiled to myself, realizing I'd have to savor this interlude of tranquility while I had the chance; it appeared my adventures weren't over after all.

I gazed broodingly at the dark blanket of storm clouds through which we were passing. Without warning, the jet broke through the somber mass into a luminous cloud canyon. Streaks of brilliant gold pierced the gloom. Patches of blue sky appeared above us; a few puffs of wispy white contrasted with the ominous gray. I recalled the colors of the Divine Mother's gown, and Brother Arthur's words — engraved eternally upon my heart — came forcefully to mind.

"Never forget that the light is infinitely more powerful than the dark. When darkness crowds in around you, become luminous, and walk in the brilliance of your soul."

I reflected on the meaning of the ancient Egyptian relic. It was an emblem representing the Possible Human — the individual imbued with Divine Power, Wisdom and Love — elevated to immortal stature. The medallion represented the eternal Wisdom, flowing as an endless river from the sacred Fount of Life. Every man and woman was called to reveal the beauty streaming forth from the paradisal realms, giving sunlight to the earth.

To become heavenly messengers — expressing celestial light and kindness — for that purpose were we predestined. Our goal, our work, our joy, was to nurture the Divine Seed planted in our hearts, bringing it to full flower, ultimately transcending death itself. Our destiny was limitless. Sublime. The greatest gift we could give was to shine light in the darkness.

"Look Daddy!" said Angelina, interrupting my musing. She took my hand and pointed out the window at the brilliant sun, which pierced the clouds with golden radiance. "I see heaven!" she said sweetly.

She held the future in her pure vision and innocent heart. I looked again at the wall of clouds. It appeared that another portal was opening. A burst of light streamed through, illuminating Angelina's face.

"Yes, treasure," I said, looking into her eyes. "And I see heaven too."

The End

"Now a great sign appeared in heaven: a woman, adorned with the sun, standing on the moon, and with the twelve stars on her head for a crown."

—St. John the Divine, *The Book Of Revelation*

A VISION

One day the chill wind whistled loud through clumps of leafless trees.
I forced my way through thorns and brush and fought against the breeze.
In frenzy I sought solitude, and deep in thought remained;
My mind, with heaviness imbued, with weariness was strained.

There came a flash of brilliant light which stunned me with its glare,
And when I had regained my sight I saw an angel fair.
Overcome with fear and awe I knelt upon the soil,
And gazed upon the visitor so dazzling and royal.

The angel spoke, she raised her hand, a glowing cloud appeared,
Replaced by yet a stranger sight when all the mist had cleared.
Before my awestruck gaze unfurled, as if in one vast plain,
Were all the countries of the world upon a grand terrain.

Europe and America were plainly to be seen,
With tides of the Atlantic gently tossing in between.
Westward the Pacific lay beyond the coastal sands,
Her deep, blue billows, tossing spray, rolled to the Asian lands.

There above the Pacific Sea, suspended in the air,
The angel hovered gracefully, luminous and fair.
She reached into the glistening sea's wide rippling, rhythmic tide,
And sprinkled water, cool with breeze, on lands at either side.

Instantly on land appeared the people of the earth;
I could see with vision clear each single person's worth.
They struggled blindly forward to some unknown, hidden goal;
Most were weak with illness and were sorrowful of soul.

A brackish cloud of ignorance hung 'round them like a cloud,
And kept them from the truths with which their spirits were endowed.
I knew it was our current age of darkness, pain and gloom —
Of misery that chained the world as if inside a tomb.

Then the angel mighty took a trumpet in her hand,
And blew three blasts resoundingly o'er water and o'er land.
Then drew she water from the sea and sprinkled drops like rain;
At once another vision formed within my mind and brain.

I saw upon a new-formed land a proud and mighty race;
Wisdom sat upon each brow, and Love upon each face.
One face distinctly I did see, 'twas fair and strong and good.
I knew at once that it was me and then I understood.

The angel looked upon the scene, her glance with love endowed.
She glowed with countenance serene and spoke these words aloud:
"Son of Light, record these words and images you see,
Of ages past and present, and of ages yet to be."

With these words the vision fled; I bowed my head, serene.
The angel left me there alone to muse on what I'd seen.
Across the ages earth revolves through pain and tragedy;
The spirit light in each evolves until we all stand free.

All those who seek a future grand and see with sacred sight
Shall forge from this tired earth of pain a globe of living light.
The future of our race is blest, transcending mortal thought;
And nothing worthy was in vain that I had ever sought.

Majestic is our life — and good — a Heavenly Romance,
And all of us are partners in a Universal Dance.
Our future 'midst the stars is certain — glorious and free;
And we will wear a Crown of Life, and love eternally.

—E. J. Michael

BIBLIOGRAPHY
SUGGESTED READING
and RESOURCES

"A word to the wise is sufficient; the rest of us need books." E.J.M.

Aivanov, O. M. GOLDEN RULES FOR EVERYDAY LIFE, Editions Prosveta, France, 1990

Allen, Gary. NONE DARE CALL IT CONSPIRACY, Concord Press, Seal Beach, CA, 1972

Ausubel, Kenny. SEEDS OF CHANGE, Harper Collins, San Francisco, CA, 1994

Bailey, Alice. INITIATION, HUMAN AND SOLAR, Lucis, New York, NY, 1951

Arguelles, Jose. THE MAYAN FACTOR, Bear and Co., Santa Fe, NM, 1987

Brinkley, Dannion. SAVED BY THE LIGHT, Villard Books, New York, NY, 1994

Carter, Forrest. THE EDUCATION OF LITTLETREE, Univ. of New Mexico Press, Albuquerque, NM. 1976

Carter, J. Edwin. LIVING IS FOREVER, Hampton Roads Press, Norfolk, VA, 1990

Chaney, Earlyne. INITIATION IN THE GREAT PYRAMID, Astara, Upland, CA, 1987

Chaney, Earlyne. REVELATIONS OF THINGS TO COME, Astara, Upland, CA, 1982

Charlton, Hilda. SAINTS ALIVE, Golden Quest, Woodstock, NY, 1989

Collins, Mabel. THE IDYLL OF THE WHITE LOTUS, Theosophical Publishing, Wheaton, Ill., 1974

Friends of Peter, THE MAGIC MAN. Roaring Lion, Gatlinburg, TN, 1990

Gray, John, MEN ARE FROM MARS, WOMEN ARE FROM VENUS. Harper Collins, New York, NY, 1992

Haich, Elisabeth. INITIATION, The Seed Center, Palo Alto, CA, 1974

Ingerman, Sandra. SOUL RETRIEVAL, Harper Collins, San Francisco, CA, 1991

King, Godfre Ray. ORIGINAL UNVEILED MYSTERIES, St. Germain Press, Schaumburg, Ill, 1982

Kirkwood, Annie. MARY'S MESSAGE TO THE WORLD, Blue Dolphin, Nevada City, CA, 1991

Kirkwood, Byron. SURVIVAL GUIDE FOR THE NEW MILLENIUM, Blue Dolphin, Nevada City, CA, 1993

Kirkwood, Byron and Annie. MARY'S MESSAGE/NEWSLETTER and B&A Products, Carrollton, TX 75011-1249, (214) 416-0141

Lash, John. THE SEEKER'S HANDBOOK, Harmony Books, New York, NY, 1990

Lorimer, David. PROPHET FOR OUR TIMES, Element, Rockport, MA 1991

Markides, Kyriacos. THE MAGUS OF STROVOLOS. Arkana/Penguin, New York, NY, 1985

Mathews, Caitlin. SOPHIA: GODDESS OF WISDOM, Aquarian Press, London, England, 1992

McFadden, Steven. PROFILES IN WISDOM, Bear and Co., Santa Fe, NM, 1991

Melchisidek, Drunvalo. SACRED GEOMETRY AND THE TEACHING OF THE MERKABAH, (Lecture Series)

Men, Hunbatz. SECRETS OF MAYAN SCIENCE AND RELIGION, Bear and Co., Santa Fe, NM, 1990

Nicolov, Nicolo. THE WORLD CONSPIRACY: WHAT THE HISTORIANS DON'T TELL YOU, Nicolov, Box 784, Portland, OR

Rain, Mary Summer. PHOENIX RISING, Hampton Roads Pub., Norfolk, VA, 1993

Ravenscroft, Trevor. THE SPEAR OF DESTINY, Samuel Weiser, New York, NY, 1972

Russell, Lao. LOVE, Univ. of Science and Philosophy, Waynesboro, VA. 1966

Scallion, Gordon-Michael. EARTH CHANGES REPORT (monthly newsletter), Matrix Institute, P.O. Box 87 Westmoreland, NH 03467, (603) 399-4916

Seeds of Change Catalog, PO Box 15700, Santa Fe, NM 87506-5700, 505-983-8956 (100% certified organically-grown seeds)

Shaw, Connie. LIGHTWAVE (quarterly newsletter) P.O. Box 548, Johnstown, CO, 80534

Shaw, Connie. MARY'S MESSAGE TO AMERICA (cassette) Om Productions, Johnstown, CO, 1993

Stanford, Ray. FATIMA PROPHECY. Ballantine, New York, 1988

Sun Bear. BLACK DAWN, BRIGHT DAY, Simon and Schuster, New York, 1992

Steiner, Rudolf. KNOWLEDGE OF HIGHER WORLDS AND ITS ATTAINMENT, Anthroposophic Press, New York, 1947

Steiner, Rudolf. VERSES AND MEDITATIONS, Rudolf Steiner Press, London, 1961

Steiner, Rudolf. WORLD HISTORY, Anthroposophic Press, NY 1968

Timms, Moira. BEYOND PROPHECIES AND PREDICTIONS, Ballantine, New York, 1994

White Eagle. SPIRITUAL UNFOLDMENT, Volumes I-IV, White Eagle Pub. Trust, Hampshire, England, 1961-1993

Wilgus, Neal. THE ILLUMINOIDS, Sun Books, Santa Fe, NM, 1978

Wolfe, Amber. THE TRUTH ABOUT SHAMANISM, Llewellyn, St.Paul, MN, 1991

Zitko, Howard John. LEMURIAN THEO-CHRISTIC CONCEPTION. World University, Benson AZ, 1936

For more copies of QUEEN OF THE SUN, or the books listed above, consult your local bookstore, or contact: **Lifeways Books and Gifts, 111 South Cortez, Prescott, AZ 86303, (602)-445-5053**

ORDER FORM

Mountain Rose Publishing
P.O. Box 2738
Prescott, AZ 86302
(602) 445-5056

Please use this coupon to order additional copies of **QUEEN OF THE SUN**, or phone in your order at (602) 445-5056.

QUANTITY		AMOUNT
_____	@ $12.95 ea.	_____

Shipping:	$2.00 first book	_____
	$1.00 second book	_____
	$0.50 each additional	_____
Arizona residents please add 6.0% sales tax		_____
Amount enclosed (U.S. Funds)		_____

Name: _____

Address: _____

_____

☐ I can't wait 2-4 weeks for book rate. Here is $3.00 per book for Air Mail/First Class

* To speed up phone orders, please have your Mastercard or Visa number ready.